**WILD**

Brun, Xanth's ~~~~~ ~~ Happiness, is usually a party animal. But Brun's babe Beryl's been bushwhacked by cheep hoods—and without his mate, the bird's got blues enough to lie down and die . . . yet without Brun's blessing, young Max and Onda's impending marriage will be a dead duck!

Max and Onda's magics *must* find the lost lovebird before Brun perishes from passion! They dare not chicken out in their wild goose chase through Xanth, menaced by foul moods, galloping miseries, discouraging words, and high anxieties . . . seeking the evil nestnapper in a place where allusion, illusion, and delusion meet in a sorcerous confrontation between the forces of write and wrong, better and verse, crime . . .

And pun-ishment . . .

CROSSROADS™ ADVENTURES are authorized interactive novels compatible for use with any role-playing game. Constructed by the masters of modern gaming, CROSSROADS™ feature complete rules; *full use* of gaming values—strength, intelligence, wisdom/luck, constitution, dexterity, charisma, and hit points; and multiple pathways for each option, for the most complete experience in gaming books, as fully realized, motivated heroes quest through the most famous worlds of fantasy!

### All new. With an introduction by PIERS ANTHONY

### ENTER THE ADVENTURE!

# TOR'S CROSSROADS™ ADVENTURE SERIES

# A CROSSROADS ADVENTURE

in the World of
## PIERS ANTHONY'S XANTH

# GHOST OF A CHANCE

by
## Jody Lynn Nye

TOR®

A TOM DOHERTY ASSOCIATES BOOK
NEW YORK

GHOST OF A CHANCE

A TOR Book
Published by Tom Doherty Associates, Inc.
49 West 24 Street
New York, NY 10010

Cover art by David Cherry

ISBN: 0-812-56450-2      Can. ISBN: 0-812-56451-0

Library of Congress Catalog Card Number: 88-50345

First Edition: September 1988

Printed in the United States of America

0 9 8 7 6 5 4 3 2 1

To the other men in my life:
Dad,
Jeff,
Todd
& Dan

# INTRODUCTION
## by Piers Anthony

THIS BOOK IS not a novel, and I didn't write it. I realize that you may find this statement odd, because here is the book in your hands, and you paid good money for it or sponged it off a friend, which friend you are about to lose when you fail to return the book. It looks just like a Xanth novel, and my name is on the cover. That just goes to show the power of illusion. Let me explain.

This is actually another kind of book masquerading as a Xanth novel. It was written by a nymph masquerading as a woman. She needed a Mundane name, so she looked to see who published the first nine Xanth novels. That was a refugee from the elven folk named Judy-Lynn del Rey. So this nymph adapted that as the perfect

1

name: Jody Lynn. But what about the last name?
If she used her real one, and called herself Jody
Lynn Nymph, everyone would know, and instead of reading her book they would all be trying
to chase after her to catch a glimpse of her legs,
because that is what any sensible person does
with a nymph. Not that Jody is ashamed of her
legs; like all nymphs she has good ones. But she
wanted people to look at her book, and they
would never do that if they knew about her legs.
So she modified her last name too: on the book it
says Jody Lynn Nye. But just in case that was still
too obvious, someone put my name on the book
above hers. No sane person would ever mistake
me for a nymph! An ogre, maybe, but never a
nymph. So you see: I didn't write it, I am here
merely to help distract attention from the nymph
until you, the reader, get firmly hooked by the
book. Then it's too late for you; you're locked in
until the end. It's a magical plot, of course.

But what's this business about it not being a
novel, you ask? It certainly *looks* like a novel!
Well, I can explain that too. It is a Game-Book. It
is really a game masquerading as a novel: more of
that illusion. If you try to read it as a novel, you'll
get all confused and messed up. You have to play
the game! That's more of that Xanthly magic the
nymph has used to enchant you. There's nothing
you can do now except relax and enjoy it, as the
nymph has her way with you.

How do you play this game? Well, there will be

instructions coming up Real Soon Now for those of you who are new to this sort of thing. Just read them and do exactly what they say. Those of you who played the Xanth Gamebook, *Encyclopedia of Xanth,* already know the route, so you can skip this dull introduction and get right into the good stuff. For the rest of you I have a small clarification that may help to confuse you, thus putting you in the right frame of mind for the punishment to come.

What punishment? The punishment of unabashed, mind-rotting puns, of course! You see, my own Xanth novels are now taking a more serious turn. That means fewer puns. What, then, is to become of those puns? It really isn't safe to stifle them, as any pundit will tell you. They tend to pile up until they overwhelm you, leaving you pun-ch drunk. So you have to be pun-ctual about getting rid of them the moment you smell the pun-gency of their approach. There has to be somewhere for them to go, for the sake of sanity.

Well, they went to the Xanth Gamebooks. Here they abound in their unnatural freedom, turning critics purple with rage and bringing illicit joy to low-brow folk like the rest of us. So if you have been starved for puns in regular Xanth novels, get into the Gamebook and have an orgy! Revel in the foul language required to get out of a thicket of curse burrs. If you are young at heart, watch out for the box elders, because they—but that would be telling! Whatever you do, stay clear of the dread Ghost Writer!

But what about this small clarification I threatened you with? All right, hang on, here it comes:

These Games are played with things like Hit Points. Now I never have quite gotten this concept straight, because every time I get too close I wind up flat on my back and hurting at several points. But the way I see it, Hit Points are things you need to survive the ordeals the game throws at you. The more of them you have, the better. So you are given a certain number of them when you start, and you try to conserve them, because when you run out of them you may be in deep, er trouble.

But where are the unused Hit Points? Obviously they can't just be left lying around, because then players would steal them and win every encounter. So it stands to reason that they are stored in some hidden depot, carefully guarded by appropriate magic. Probably a vault that is camouflaged as an innocuous little shed, so that it won't attract the attention of demons who might blast it apart to get at the valuable Hit Points inside. This shed would be known as the Hit Shed, of course.

But how do legitimate parties get into it when they need their set number of Hit Points? They can't just open the door, because any demon or Hit poacher could do likewise, and steal them all. They might use a key—but demons could turn invisible, steal the key, and raid the Shed. No, it has to be some more secure device.

Such as a magic phrase. Remember how Alladin got into the Thieves horde? He said "O-pun Sesame!" and it o-punned magically. We would have to use some other phrase, of course, because that one is already known. It can't be too complicated, because then the good folk would forget it or confuse it. So instead of having a separate phrase, they might merely use a secret way of addressing the Hit Shed, such as reversing the initial sounds. Demons would never catch on to that! The Shed will open only when it hears the correct reversal. Thus the person approaches the door and proclaims "Hit Shed!" only with the initial sound re—

Then again, maybe I had better stick to writing novels. Enjoy your Game with the Nymph!

# INTRODUCTION AND RULES TO CROSSROADS™ ADVENTURES
## by Bill Fawcett

FOR THE MANY of us who have enjoyed the stories upon which this adventure is based, it may seem a bit strange to find an introduction this long at the start of a book. What you are holding is both a game and an adventure. Have you ever read a book and then told yourself you would have been able to think more clearly or seen a way out of the hero's dilemma? In a Crossroads™ adventure you have the opportunity to do just that. *You* make the key decisions. By means of a few easily followed steps you are able to see the results of your choices.

A Crossroads™ adventure is as much fun to read as it is to play. It is more than just a game or a book. It is a chance to enjoy once more a familiar and treasured story. The excitement of adventuring in a beloved universe is neatly blended into a story which stands well on its own merit, a story in which you will encounter many familiar characters and places and discover more than a few new ones as well. Each adventure is a thrilling tale, with the extra suspense and satisfaction of knowing that you will succeed or fail by your own endeavors.

## THE ADVENTURE

Throughout the story you will have the opportunity to make decisions. Each of these decisions will affect whether the hero succeeds in the quest, or even survives. In some cases you will actually be fighting battles; other times you will use your knowledge and instincts to choose the best path to follow. In many cases there will be clues in the story or illustrations.

A Crossroads™ adventure is divided into sections. The length of a section may be a few lines or many pages. The section numbers are shown at the top of a page to make it easier for you to follow. Each section ends when you must make a decision, or fight. The next section you turn to will show the results of your decision. At least one six-sided die and a pencil are needed to "play" this book.

The words "six-sided dice" are often abbreviated as "D6." If more than one is needed, a number will precede the term. "Roll three six-sided dice" will be written as "Roll 3 D6."

Virtually all the die rolls in these rules do involve rolling three six-sided dice (or rolling one six-sided die three times) and totaling what is rolled.

If you are an experienced role-play gamer, you may also wish to convert the values given in this novel to those you can use with any fantasy role-playing game you are now playing with. All of the adventures have been constructed so that they also can be easily adapted in this manner. The values for the hero may transfer directly. While fantasy games are much more complicated, doing this will allow you to be the Game Master for other players. Important values for the hero's opponents will be given to aid you in this conversion and to give those playing by the Crossroads™ rules a better idea of what they are facing.

## THE HERO

Seven values are used to describe the hero in gaming terms. These are strength, intelligence, wisdom/luck, constitution, dexterity, charisma, and hit points. These values measure all of a character's abilities. At the end of these rules is a record sheet. On it are given all of the values for the hero of this adventure and any equipment or supplies they begin the adventure with. While you adventure, this record can be used to keep track of damage received and any new equipment or magical items acquired. You may find it advisable to make a photocopy of that page. Permission to do so, for your own use only, is given by the publisher of this game/novel. You may wish to consult this record sheet as we discuss what each of the values represents.

## STRENGTH

This is the measure of how physically powerful your hero is. It compares the hero to others in how much the character can lift, how hard he can punch, and just how brawny he is. The strongest a normal human can be is to have a strength value of 18. The weakest a child would have is a 3. Here is a table giving comparable strengths:

| Strength | Example |
| --- | --- |
| 3 | A 5-year-old child |
| 6 | An elderly man |
| 8 | Out of shape and over 40 |
| 10 | An average 20-year-old man |
| 13 | In good shape and works out |
| 15 | A top athlete or football running back |
| 17 | Changes auto tires without a jack |
| 18 | Arm wrestles Arnold Schwarzenegger and wins |

A Tolkien-style troll, being magical, might have a strength of 19 or 20. A full-grown elephant has a strength of 23. A fifty-foot dragon would have a strength of 30.

# INTELLIGENCE

Being intelligent is not just a measure of native brain power. It is also an indication of the ability to use that intelligence. The value for intelligence also measures how aware the character is, and so how likely they are to notice a subtle clue. Intelligence can be used to measure how resistant a mind is to hypnosis or mental attack. A really sharp baboon would have an intelligence of 3. Most humans (we all know exceptions) begin at about 5. The highest value possible is an 18. Here is a table of relative intelligence:

| Intelligence | Example |
| --- | --- |
| 3 | My dog |
| 5 | Lassie |
| 6 | Curly (the third Stooge) |
| 8 | Somewhat slow |
| 10 | Average person |
| 13 | College professor/good quarterback |
| 15 | Indiana Jones/Carl Sagan |
| 17 | Doc Savage/Mr. Spock |
| 18 | Leonardo dá Vinci (Isaac Asimov?) |

Brainiac of comic-book fame would have a value of 21.

# WISDOM/LUCK

Wisdom is the ability to make correct judgments, often with less than complete facts. Wisdom is knowing what to do and when to do it. Attacking, when running will earn you a spear in the back, is the best part of wisdom. Being in the right place at the right time can be called luck or wisdom. Not being discovered when hiding can be luck, if it is because you knew enough to not hide in the poison oak, wisdom is also a factor. Activities which are based more on instinct, the intuitive leap, than analysis are decided by wisdom.

In many ways both wisdom and luck are further connected, especially as wisdom also measures how friendly the ruling powers of the universe (not the author, the fates) are to the hero. A hero may be favored by fate or luck because he is reverent or for no discernible reason at all. This will give them a high wisdom value. Everyone knows those "lucky" individuals who can fall in the mud and find a gold coin. Here is a table measuring relative wisdom/luck:

| Wisdom | Example |
| --- | --- |
| Under 3 | Cursed or totally unthinking |
| 5 | Never plans, just reacts |
| 7 | Some cunning, "street smarts" |
| 9 | Average thinking person |
| 11 | Skillful planner, good gambler |

| | |
|---|---|
| 13 | Successful businessman/Lee Iacocca |
| 15 | Captain Kirk (wisdom)/Conan (luck) |
| 17 | Sherlock Holmes (wisdom)/Luke Skywalker (luck) |
| 18 | Lazarus Long |

## CONSTITUTION

The more you can endure, the higher your constitution. If you have a high constitution you are better able to survive physical damage, emotional stress, and poisons. The higher your value for constitution, the longer you are able to continue functioning in a difficult situation. A character with a high constitution can run farther (though not necessarily faster) or hang by one hand longer than the average person. A high constitution means you also have more stamina, and recover more quickly from injuries. A comparison of values for constitution:

| Constitution | Example |
|---|---|
| 3 | A terminal invalid |
| 6 | A 10-year-old child |
| 8 | Your stereotyped "98-pound weakling" |
| 10 | Average person |
| 14 | Olympic athlete/Sam Spade |

| 16 | Marathon runner/Rocky |
| 18 | Rasputin/Batman |

A whale would have a constitution of 20. Superman's must be about 50.

# DEXTERITY

The value for dexterity measures not only how fast a character can move, but how well-coordinated those movements are. A surgeon, a pianist, and a juggler all need a high value for dexterity. If you have a high value for dexterity you can react quickly (though not necessarily correctly), duck well, and perform sleight-of-hand magic (if you are bright enough to learn how). Conversely, a low dexterity means you react slowly and drop things frequently. All other things being equal, the character with the highest dexterity will have the advantage of the first attack in a combat. Here are some comparative examples of dexterity:

| Dexterity | Example |
|---|---|
| 3 or less | Complete klutz |
| 5 | Inspector Clouseau |
| 6 | Can walk and chew gum, most of the time |
| 8 | Barney Fife |
| 10 | Average person |

| 13 | Good fencer/Walter Payton |
| 15 | Brain surgeon/Houdini |
| 16 | Flying Karamazov Brothers |
| 17 | Movie ninja/Cyrano de Bergerac |
| 18 | Bruce Lee |

Batman, Robin, Daredevil and The Shadow all have a dexterity of 19. At a dexterity of 20 you don't even see the man move before he has taken your wallet and underwear and has left the room (the Waco Kid).

## CHARISMA

Charisma is more than just good looks, though they certainly don't hurt. It is a measure of how persuasive a hero is and how willing others are to do what he wants. You can have average looks yet be very persuasive, and have a high charisma. If your value for charisma is high, you are better able to talk yourself out of trouble or obtain information from a stranger. If your charisma is low, you may be ignored or even mocked, even when you are right. A high charisma value is vital to entertainers of any sort, and leaders. A different type of charisma is just as important to spies. In the final measure a high value for charisma means people will react to you in the way you desire. Here are some comparative values for charisma:

| Charisma | Example |
|----------|---------|
| 3 | Hunchback of Notre Dame |
| 5 | An ugly used-car salesman |
| 7 | Richard Nixon today |
| 10 | Average person |
| 12 | Team coach |
| 14 | Magnum, P.I. |
| 16 | Henry Kissinger/Jim DiGriz |
| 18 | Dr. Who/Prof. Harold Hill (Centauri) |

# HIT POINTS

Hit points represent the total amount of damage a hero can take before he is killed or knocked out. You can receive damage from being wounded in a battle, through starvation, or even through a mental attack. Hit points measure more than just how many times the hero can be battered over the head before he is knocked out. They also represent the ability to keep striving toward a goal. A poorly paid mercenary may have only a few hit points, even though he is a hulking brute of a man, because the first time he receives even a slight wound he will withdraw from the fight. A blacksmith's apprentice who won't accept defeat will have a higher number of hit points.

A character's hit points can be lost through a wound to a specific part of the body or through general damage to the body itself. This general damage can be caused by a poison, a bad fall, or even exhaustion and starvation. Pushing your body too far beyond its limits may result in a successful action at the price of the loss of a few hit points. All these losses are treated in the same manner.

Hit points lost are subtracted from the total on the hero's record sheet. When a hero has lost all of his hit points, then that character has failed. When this happens you will be told to which section to turn. Here you will often find a description of the failure and its consequences for the hero.

The hit points for the opponents the hero meets in combat are given in the adventure. You should keep track of these hit points on a piece of scrap paper. When a monster or opponent has lost all of their hit points, they have lost the fight. If a character is fighting more than one opponent, then you should keep track of each of their hit points. Each will continue to fight until it has 0 hit points. When everyone on one side of the battle has no hit points left, the combat is over.

Even the best played character can lose all of his hit points when you roll too many bad dice during a combat. If the hero loses all of his hit points, the adventure may have ended in failure. You will be told so in the next section you are instructed to turn to. In this case you can turn back to the first section and begin again.

This time you will have the advantage of having learned some of the hazards the hero will face.

## TAKING CHANCES

There will be occasions where you will have to decide whether the hero should attempt to perform some action which involves risk. This might be to climb a steep cliff, jump a pit, or juggle three daggers. There will be other cases where it might benefit the hero to notice something subtle or remember an ancient ballad perfectly. In all of these cases you will be asked to roll three six-sided dice (3 D6) and compare the total of all three dice to the hero's value for the appropriate ability.

For example, if the hero is attempting to juggle three balls, then for him to do so successfully you would have to roll a total equal to or less than the hero's value for dexterity. If your total was less than this dexterity value, then you would be directed to a section describing how the balls looked as they were skillfully juggled. If you rolled a higher value than that for dexterity, then you would be told to read a section which describes the embarrassment of dropping the balls, and being laughed at by the audience.

Where the decision is a judgment call, such as whether to take the left or right staircase, it is left entirely to you. Somewhere in the adventure or in the original novels there will be some piece of information which would indicate that the left staircase leads to a trap and the right to your goal. No die roll will be needed for a judgment decision.

In all cases you will be guided at the end of each section as to exactly what you need do. If you have any questions you should refer back to these rules.

## MAGICAL ITEMS AND SPECIAL EQUIPMENT

There are many unusual items which appear in the pages of this adventure. When it is possible for them to be taken by the hero, you will be given the option of doing so. One or more of these items may be necessary to the successful completion of the adventure. You will be given the option of taking these at the end of a section. If you choose to pick up an item and succeed in getting it, you should list that item on the hero's record sheet. There is no guarantee that deciding to take an item means you will actually obtain it. If someone owns it already they are quite likely to resent your efforts to take it. In some cases things may not even be all they appear to be or the item may be trapped or cursed. Having it may prove a detriment rather than a benefit.

All magical items give the hero a bonus (or

penalty) on certain die rolls. You will be told when this applies, and often given the option of whether or not to use the item. You will be instructed at the end of the section on how many points to add to or subtract from your die roll. If you choose to use an item which can function only once, such as a magic potion or hand grenade, then you will also be instructed to remove the item from your record sheet. Certain items, such as a magic sword, can be used many times. In this case you will be told when you obtain the item when you can apply the bonus. The bonus for a magic sword could be added every time a character is in hand-to-hand combat.

Other special items may allow a character to fly, walk through fire, summon magical warriors, or many other things. How and when they affect play will again be told to you in the paragraphs at the end of the sections where you have the choice of using them.

Those things which restore lost hit points are a special case. You may choose to use these at any time during the adventure. If you have a magical healing potion which returns 1 D6 of lost hit points, you may add these points when you think it is best to. This can even be during a combat in the place of a round of attack. No matter how many healing items you use, a character can never have more hit points than he begins the adventure with.

There is a limit to the number of special item any character may carry. In any Crossroads™ adventure the limit is four items. If you alread have four special items listed on your recor sheet, then one of these must be discarded i order to take the new item. Any time you erase a item off the record sheet, whether because it wa used or because you wish to add a new item whatever is erased is permanently lost. It ca never be "found" again, even if you return to th same location later in the adventure.

Except for items which restore hit points, th hero can only use an item in combat or whe given the option to do so. The opportunity wil be listed in the instructions.

In the case of an item which can be used i every combat, the bonus can be added or sub tracted as the description of the item indicates. A +2 sword would add two points to any tota rolled in combat. This bonus would be used each and every time the hero attacks. Only one attack bonus can be used at a time. Just because a here has both a +1 and a +2 sword doesn't mean he knows how to fight with both at once. Only the better bonus would apply.

If a total of 12 is needed to hit an attackin monster and the hero has a +2 sword, then you will only need to roll a total of 10 on the three dice to successfully strike the creature.

You could also find an item, perhaps en chanted armor, which could be worn in all combat and would have the effect of subtracting its bonus from the total of any opponent's attack on its wearer. (Bad guys can wear magic armor, too.) If a monster normally would need a 13 to hit a character who has obtained a set of +2 armor, then the monster would now need a total of 15 to score a hit. An enchanted shield would operate in the same way, but could never be used when the character was using a weapon which needed both hands, such as a pike, longbow, or two-handed sword.

## COMBAT

There will be many situations where the hero will be forced, or you may choose, to meet an opponent in combat. The opponents can vary from a wild beast, to a human thief, or an unearthly monster. In all cases the same steps are followed.

The hero will attack first in most combats unless you are told otherwise. This may happen when there is an ambush, other special situations, or because the opponent simply has a much higher dexterity.

At the beginning of a combat section you will be given the name or type of opponent involved. For each combat five values are given. The first of these is the total on three six-sided dice needed for the attacker to hit the hero. Next to this value is the value the hero needs to hit these opponents. After these two values is listed the hit points of the opponent. If there is more than one opponent, each one will have the same number. (See the Hit Points section included earlier if you are unclear as to what these do.) Under the value needed to be hit by the opponent is the hit points of damage that it will do to the hero when it attacks successfully. Finally, under the total needed for the hero to successfully hit an opponent is the damage he will do with the different weapons he might have. Unlike a check for completing a daring action (where you wish to roll under a value), in a combat you have to roll the value given or higher on three six-sided dice to successfully hit an opponent.

For example:

Here is how a combat between the hero armed with a sword and three brigands armed only with daggers is written:

BRIGANDS

*To hit the hero: 14　To be hit: 12　Hit points: 4*

*Damage with daggers: 1 D6 (used by the brigands)*　*Damage with sword: 2 D6 (used by the hero)*

*There are three brigands. If two are killed (taken to 0 hit points) the third will flee in panic.*

*If the hero wins, turn to section 85.*

*If he is defeated, turn to section 67.*

# RUNNING AWAY

Running rather than fighting, while often desirable, is not always possible. The option to run away is available only when listed in the choices. Even when this option is given, there is no guarantee the hero can get away safely.

# THE COMBAT SEQUENCE

Any combat is divided into alternating rounds. In most cases the hero will attack first. Next, surviving opponents will have the chance to fight back. When both have attacked, one round will have been completed. A combat can have any number of rounds and continues until the hero or his opponents are defeated. Each round is the equivalent of six seconds. During this time all the parties in the combat may actually take more than one swing at each other.

The steps in resolving a combat in which the hero attacks first are as follows:

1. Roll three six-sided dice. Total the numbers showing on all three and add any bonuses

from weapons or special circumstances. If this total is the same or greater than the second value given, "to hit the opponent," then the hero has successfully attacked.

2. If the hero attacks successfully, the next step is to determine how many hit points of damage he did to the opponent. The die roll for this will be given below the "to hit opponent" information.

3. Subtract any hit points of damage done from the opponent's total.

4. If any of the enemy have one or more hit points left, then the remaining opponent or opponents now can attack. Roll three six-sided dice for each attacker. Add up each of these sets of three dice. If the total is the same as, or greater than the value listed after "to hit the hero" in the section describing the combat, the attack was successful.

5. For each hit, roll the number of dice listed for damage. Subtract the total from the number of hit points the hero has at that time. Enter the new, lower total on the hero's record sheet.

If both the hero and one or more opponents have hit points left, the combat continues. Start again at step one. The battle ends only when the hero is killed, all the opponents are killed, or all of one side has run away. A hero cannot, except through a healing potion or spells or when specifically told to during the adventure, regain lost hit points. A number of small wounds from several opponents will kill a character as thoroughly as one titanic, unsuccessful combat with a hill giant.

## DAMAGE

The combat continues, following the sequence given below, until either the hero or his opponents have no hit points. In the case of multiple opponents, subtract hit points from one opponent until the total reaches 0 or less. Extra hit points of damage done on the round when each opponent is defeated are lost. They do not carry over to the next enemy in the group. To win the combat, you must eliminate all of an opponent's hit points.

The damage done by a weapon will vary depending on who is using it. A club in the hands of a child will do far less damage than the same club wielded by a hill giant. The maximum damage is given as a number of six-sided dice. In some cases the maximum will be less than a whole die. This is abbreviated by a minus sign followed by a number. For example D6−2, meaning one roll of a six-sided die, minus two. The total damage can never be less than zero, meaning no damage done. 2 D6−1 means that you should roll two six-sided dice and then subtract one from the total of them both.

A combat may, because of the opponent involved, have one or more special circumstances. It may be that the enemy will surrender or flee when its hit point total falls below a certain level, or even that reinforcements will arrive to help the bad guys after so many rounds. You will be told of these special situations in the lines directly under the combat values.

Now you may turn to section 1.

# RECORD SHEET

## Max

___

Strength:  14          Age:  25
Intelligence:  13
Wisdom/Luck:  13       Hit Points: 23
Constitution:  12
Dexterity:  11
Charisma:  14

Weapons Carried:         Magical Items:
1. tire iron             1. fast overland snail in
                            box
2. icicle                2.
3.                       3.

Other items carried:
1. basket
2. pocket knife
3.
4.

In the Hope Chest:
1.

Special: Max is a citizen of Xanth. His magical talent is his lantern jaw, which he can illuminate any time he wishes. Its magic ranges from a very dim light to a near-searchlight strength beam.

## * **1** *

"It's my wedding day," Max exclaims, opening his eyes and smiling at the ceiling. He rises to one elbow and looks around the room. This is the house he built for himself and his new bride. Oh, it's bare of fur-niture yet, but the fur hasn't had time to grow. He and his wife-to-be will just have to do with makeshift household goods until then. With a smile, he conjures a vision of Onda from his memory and admires it. She certainly is the most beautiful girl in Xanth. Such lovely, soft red hair, blue eyes brighter than the sky, and what a figure—!

"I'm the luckiest of men," Max tells his mirror reflection, rubbing a hand along his lantern jaw and feeling the whiskers. "Hmmm. Time to shave."

Yawning and stretching, he pulls the door open. The sunlight is bright, and the sky is clear. A perfect day for a wedding. Outside, the little yard is full of rowan in rows and columbine in columns totting up sums, and button flowers all done up neatly; all manner of things that Onda loves.

Max laughs when he sees the gate of his yard. It has been hung with dozens of shoes so ancient and decrepit that there are shoe-flies circling them. Symbols of good luck have been placed everywhere by his well-wishers. To Max, all the good luck he'll need is embodied by Onda, though the blessing of the Bluebird of Happiness will help contribute to his feeling of well-being.

In the South Village, where he lives, it is the custom for the Bluebird to bless each marriage to ensure its happiness. It isn't considered really to be a marriage if the Bluebird doesn't attend. The bird casts its aura of joy all over the village, so everyone has a good time. Lots of other marriages are usually proposed during the celebration. Each village has it own Bluebird, though the customs from place to place vary. The species gravitates toward human beings. Probably they were adapted by King Roogna from a magical bird that spread happiness generally, the way a grouse does, only in a positive note. He just concentrated the effect directionally. King Roogna's talent was magical adaptation.

Other beasts and living things were adapted by the King during the Golden Age of Xanth; things which made life for its citzens easier to live. Max searches around his yard and finally throws back his head to whistle a signal. In answer, he hears eager grunting. Emil, his pet razorback pig, comes running out from the side of the little wall-nut cottage. Max scratches the pig between his sharply pointed ears and breaks off a fresh razor from the profusion along Emil's spine. Fitting the blade-shaped scale into a holder in his room, he skims some fresh whisker cream off the

op of a bucket of milk from his wire-haired cow
and lathers up, smearing the foam across his
lower face.

"Hmm," Max grumbles around the blade,
"not enough light." It is especially important
that he does a good job today and remove every
black whisker on his chin. He wants to look his
best at the ceremony.

Concentrating, he illumines his lantern jaw
and happily finishes the shave up evenly all
around. His black stubble shows up very clearly
on the lighted surface. Max's talent is the ability
to radiate light from his chin and the lower parts
of his face. He was embarrassed in his youth
when the talent first manifested itself, but it
turned out to be very useful for reading under the
covers after his parents had put out the lights. As
a result of so much surreptitious reading, he was
very well educated when he reached his majori-
ty. His fiancée proved to be as much attracted by
his lantern jaw as by his intelligence. Her own
talent is that of manifesting directional assist-
ance on the tops of her hands. Whenever she
needs to find her way into or out of any place, she
has a small map appear and instantly knows
every location like the back of her hand. Max
never needs to fear Onda getting lost.

Putting on his shower cap, he walks around the
house preparing breakfast. Under the scone stone
in the pantry, he finds a few freshly laid biscuits,
which he smears thickly with honey gathered
from the last honeymoon that shone in the sky

## Section 1

over Xanth. Gathering honey is a sticky business even when using honey combs to comb it out of the sky, but Xanth citizens consider it to be worth while. Supplying sweet things in Xanth is hive-volume business.

The water cascading down from the shower cap rushes down his body to his feet and sweeps back up into the cap again, sluicing his skin clean. The water doesn't get all over because the cap's magic keeps it contained. Feeling refreshed, he removes the cap and towels himself off with flannel from his towel horse. Wringing a bay leaf between his fingers, he dabs bay rum over his skin as a tonic. Max ignores the mournful howl of the bay bush; he's too happy to hear anything but joyful noises today. Even the scones with honey taste better than they usually do.

Outside, he goes to fetch his wedding clothes, which are lying on a flat drying stone that makes up the second half of his combination washer/dryer that he brought to his new cottage from his old family home. The washing powder is still causing the water in his little pond to wash up and down against the banks. Its action beats the grime out of anything that he puts into the water, dishes, clothes, tools. On the whole, the setup has been terrific for a bachelor such as himself. It isn't a very big drying stone, so he has to straighten out the creases in the fabric by applying the clothes to the ironwood tree that grows nearby. Onda may want to find a larger rock.

His evening dinner dishes are spotless, and he

takes the rack out of the pond and places it on the drying stone to air out. The feast to celebrate his marriage will last all day long, so he won't need the dishes today. His and Onda's first meal together in the little cottage will probably be in the morning, after . . . well, it was better not to think about that too much! With care, he puts the dishes away, and goes to don his wedding clothes in front of his mirror.

Within a short time, Max is ready. His chores take up very little time: sharpening Emil's scales, milking the little cow, and looking in on his animal patients. Ever since he was a child, Max has displayed a real love for animals that almost amounts to a second talent, in the opinion of his neighbors, so he has been the village animal doctor for some years now. His most puzzling case, that of an angle worm belonging to the village carpenter that can only draw curves, is responding well to a diet of square roots and boxwood leaves from the boxwoods that make up Max's little cottage.

Max makes his way to the town square. The bluebells that twine up and down the brightly shining hornbeam trees growing along the path ring loudly as he goes by, and the hornbeams honk companionably at him. Even the usually rambunctious buckeyes wink. Max is a very popular man. His friends and neighbors will all be at the ceremony, arrayed in their very best festival clothes, though none could be so splendidly dressed as he. His boots are of softly brushed blue suede, that causes him to sway from side to side as he walks, but the effect is worth the inconvenience. Max's purple trousers and matching waistcoat are positively fit for a bridegroom. The splendid white shirt, plucked only a few days ago from a cultured shirt tree, is embroidered with spectacularly scenic tales by a woman named Liza. She's the finest liar in the village, and her talent enables her to transform her yarns into beautiful pictures. With her mendacious skill, Liza can fix anything that is torn.

All at once, he stumbles and falls to his knees, ripping his pants legs on the pebble path. "Oh, no, my new clothes!" He leaps up and brushes the dirt loose. Admittedly, Max hasn't been thinking where he is walking, but he's sure the place he just walked over was level. He looks behind him, and sees a shallow pit dug into the pathway. In the bushes to one side, there is mad, cackling laughter. Max strides forward and parts the bushes with angry, powerful hands. Urmund, Liza's son, is rolling around on the sward, laughing. Another ruffian, Belo, is there, too. They see Max and the damage to his fine clothes, and hoot louder. Max's eyes narrow.

"I should have known." Urmund's talent is camouflage. He can disguise anything in a small area to hide it from sight. Everyone in the village has suffered from his pranks at one time or another, crashing into trees they don't see or avoiding illusory rocks to trip over real ones. Belo is more dangerous. His talent allows him to block any one of a person's seven senses. As Max leans over to pick the two boys up by their collars, Belo gestures.

Instantly, everything goes dark. Max straightens up, temporarily distracted from seizing the pranksters. Of course, this is Belo's doing. He has blocked Max's vision.

Max can hear Urmund and Belo's hysterical chortling as they roll about, enjoying his helplessness. He's known these boys all his life, and his great fear is that they might do something else silly, perhaps tie him up and transport him somewhere far away, making him miss his own wedding.

Max's talent, his lantern jaw, is of no use to him while he is blinded. He must rely on his strength and his wits. His line of work compels him to keep in shape to deal with his larger animal patients. Unfortunately, the advantages are all on the side of the ruffians. They spin him around and around, evading his attempts to grab them, and then let go. Max staggers, hands out for obstructions, his sense of direction bewildered.

"Get the lepermud!" Urmund cries gleefully. Their footsteps pound away from him along the enchanted path.

"No!" Max yells after them. Lepermud would make him break out in hideous white patches. It

would be almost as bad as being a zombie! He'd
look horrible. But what can he do, blind as he is?

*If Max wants to run away from the bullies, turn to
section 4.*

*If Max wants to try to trounce the bullies, turn to
section 6.*

\* **2** \*

Max lunges toward the sound of Belo's voice, but
his grabbing hands close on nothing.

"Haw, haw, haw!" Urmund laughs from behind Max. Suddenly, the blind man gets booted
hard in the rear. "That mud must be eating your
brains away already!"

Max spins and charges toward Urmund's
voice. But the bully has moved, and Max crashes
into a tree.

"Honk!" protests the hornbeam.

"Sorry," Max mutters, turning around again,
but he hears only the derisive laughter and running footsteps as Belo and Urmund trot away.

Cooling his lust for vengeance, Max has to
think of how he can undo the mischief the boys
did him and still get to his wedding on time.
There is a healing spring not far away, but in
which direction?

"Let's see," Max says to himself. "I was walking along the path to the town square. There are hornbeams here—Hornbeam! Will you honk for me?" he asks.

"WHONK!" comes a noise from only a few feet to his left.

Max smiles. Clean left hand extended, he shuffles toward the sound. As if sensing his distress, the bluebells set up a tremendous clangor that grows louder as he reaches his goal.

Good, he has found the edge of the path, but how far along it is he? Well, the hornbeam he is touching hoots in a lovely E-flat, so he has scaled along just under halfway. Turning carefully around, he feels his way along the path and follows his nose to the healing spring.

His fingers are growing numb, and he worries that one or more of them might fall off before he gets to the spring, but he is afraid to touch his right hand with his unmuddy left hand to find out for fear of spreading the contagion.

It is a tense search, but finally, Max is relieved to smell the cedar-chest tree that overhangs the healing spring. He knows that the spring has a geas on it preventing anyone from telling anyone else where it is, but the warning always appears written on the water's surface.

"I promise," Max cries, knowing the caveat by heart, and plunges himself headfirst into the pond.

His eyes are the first things to recover. Belo's spell is minor magic, after all, and it doesn't take much to wash it away. Max sits up on the bank and examines his hand. To his horror, he realizes that two of his fingers have fallen off! The disgust is short-lived, since the spring's powerful magic restores lost digits in a matter of seconds. His two new fingers are better than the original ones, though they lack the deep tan of the rest of his hand. No matter. The wringing wet new ring finger is perfectly fine for putting a wedding ring on. But if he doesn't hurry, he won't have a bride waiting for him to marry! He curses Urmund and Belo for making him waste so much time.

Gathering his soiled clothes in a bag from a wheezing bagpipe bush, Max heads toward the village's dry-cleaning plant.

*Turn to section 7.*

* **3** *

Onda wrings her hands together in worry as the switchback rushes off into the trees. As soon as she is sure it is gone, she parts the leaves of the parasol tree and rushes over to her fiancé's side. "Max? Oh, Max." She kneels down and lays a delicate ear to his chest. He is still breathing, but he is deeply unconscious. His many wounds trouble her, but she has no medicines handy.

Onda sits back on her heels. She consults her talent to find a healing spring. The little map appears as ordered on the back of her hand, but she discovers to her dismay that there isn't one within an hour's walk. She won't leave Max alone that long. There is a cottonwood within sight of where she is sitting. Rising reluctantly from Max's side, Onda breaks a branch from the tree and scoops the fluffy cotton out of the hollow limb. At least she can pack Max's wounds while waiting for rescue.

Ruefully, Onda accepts the fact that she and Max have failed Brun, who was so counting on them to help him find his beloved Beryl. She must now send for help.

*Turn to section 29.*

## * **4** *

"I've got to get away from here," Max thinks. His vision is still black, but nothing has happened to his hearing. Urmund and Belo are not far away from him, and it sounds like they're dragging a big pail of lepermud his way. That slimy stuff would make him a pariah from polite society for days, or until he was able to get an antidote for the white blotches. If he was especially unlucky, one of his extremities might fall off, his nose, or his fingers, or worse! The only cures he knew of had to do with healing elixir or missionary beetles, and he wasn't fond of those boring beetles. They were as bad as praying mantises for calling down divine intervention for straightforward everyday tasks.

The best thing he can do is get away, and only if he hurries. The boys obviously think that he is helpless because he is blind and are paying no attention to him, but Max was brought up in this village, and he knows the terrain intimately. He is not helpless if he keeps his wits about him.

"Let's see," Max says to himself. "I was walking along the path to the town square. There are hornbeams here— Hornbeam! Will you honk for me?" he asks softly.

"WHONK!" comes a noise from only a few feet to his left.

Max smiles. Urmund, busy with his mischief, would think that the hornbeam was just sounding off. Hands extended, Max shuffles toward the sound. As if sensing his distress, the bluebell sets up a tremendous clangor.

"Shh!" Max pleads with the vine. It acknowledges him with a friendly little ting-a-ling.

Good, he has found the edge of the path, but how far along it is he? Well, the hornbeam he is touching hoots in a lovely E-flat, so he has scaled along just under halfway. He remembers that just off the path, behind some trees, there is thick bracken in which he can hide until the blindness wears off or until his attackers go away. It was a place he used for years to hide in when he didn't want to be found for chores. Luckily for him, and for all the denizens of the village, Belo's magic requires eye contact with his victim. If the bully can't see Max's eyes, he can't re-spell him. Uh-oh, Max thinks, they're coming back.

Blundering off the path, Max feels his way toward safety. His nose tells him he is near the food trees. The savory smells of pizza pie and hot dogwood dogs make him hungry. Max chides his stomach to silence, promising it the choicest bits from the wedding feast to come.

"Hey, watch where you're going!" a peevish voice cries out as Max stumbles.

"I'm sorry," Max says, puzzled. His hands tell him that he has just run into a tree, not a sentient being. He can't remember any talking trees planted here.

"You could knock all my tree's pies off if yer not careful, ya big oaf. Where'd ya learn to walk? On a field trip?"

"I'm trying to hide," Max explains to the unfamiliar voice. He runs his hand over the shrub next to the tree and discovers that it is a blanket bush. That'll give him plenty of cover. "You'll give me away. Please be quiet."

"Me be quiet? I'll shove some of my filling into yer big yap if ya don't treat me with more respect. That'll pucker ya," the voice went on sourly.

Filling? Max muses. It must be a talking pie. No pies made noises except burp-berries, and those only bloomed during rainstorms. The noises those make aren't exactly coherent speech, and they generally erupt after the pie has been eaten, not before. Wait, there is a kind of talking pie his centaur teacher told him about. They are rare, but he guesses that he was having a chat with one now. "You're a lemon harangue pie!"

"Give the dope a cigar. Look at you, falling all over your big feet. In two seconds you're going to lean back against that gluebark, ain'tcha? What a maroon!"

Unperturbed, Max assumes that the pie is talking about the color of his wedding clothes. Heart sinking, Max realizes that this run-in with bullies will probably make him late for the wedding. A gluebark, eh?

Cautiously, he reaches behind him and runs his fingertips along the bole of the tree which tries instantly to adhere to his skin. He pulls them away swiftly. It *is* a gluebark. What a piece of luck, Max thinks. Anything that touches that kind of tree sticks to it until and unless the tree decides to let go. Max cocks an ear toward the path. Belo and Urmund have returned, and they are looking for him. They haven't yet thought of straying off the path. Well, he can fox those two now, if he is clever.

"Listen, pie," Max says, out of the corner of his mouth. "You see those two guys over there?"

"What about 'em? They look just like you, only dumber." A pause for consideration. "Naw, I take that back. *You* look dumber."

"Well, they say that a lemon harangue pie is

the most foolish kind of pie that ever budded on a decent tree. They say that the only reason your kind grow to maturity instead of being plucked eagerly while still young tarts is because only a moron would eat something like you when there were stale spinach beans still lying around." Max grins at the indignant piping of the hot pie and wishes he could see it steam.

"They do, do they?" The pie is cracking its shell in fury. "Hey, you big oafs! And do you want to know what I think of half-wit humans anyway?"

Letting the furious pastry go on with its verbal pasting, Max crouches down and backs carefully into the blanket bush, being careful to draw some of the leaves in front of him, and hopes that he hasn't left any open places to give him away. The scratchy branches and smooth, fleecy blankets swish softly as they fall into place around him. He is just in time, too, for the two bullies come threshing through the woods, lured by the angry lemon pie's harangue.

"Who's yelling?" Belo yells, his footsteps arriving just before those of his crony.

"Me, you crustless wonder," the pie rages.

"Aw, look at that," Urmund snickers. "A tough cooky, all tarted up."

Max waits until the three of them are engrossed in insulting each other, and then he leaps up out of the bush and shoves with all his strength at whatever is in front of him. He is very strong but always reluctant to use force against sentient beings. In this case, though, he feels safe letting himself go.

Surprise is on his side. With surprised howls, Belo and Urmund topple over. Gloop! Gloop! Max knows just by the sound that they have fallen against the gluebark.

"Max!" Urmund growls. Then, realizing that the advantage has changed sides, alters his tone to one of sticky sweetness. "Max, old pal. Old buddy. You wouldn't leave two of your oldest friends here to be gobbled up by a messy old glue tree, would you?"

Feeling behind him surreptitiously with one hand, Max leans casually against the blanket bush. "Well, who's there?" he asks, turning his head from side to side. "I'm sorry. It sounds like Urmund, but I can't tell. I can't see, you see."

"Aw, for peat's sake," Urmund swears. He was always an earthy type. "Take the spell off, Belo."

"No. Not until he makes the gluebark let us go."

Max shakes his head. "Sorry. I don't release you unless you take the spell off. I'm late already. I may just have to go and get married and let my eyesight return slowly over time. It won't bother me. I've been on blind dates before. Adds a little . . . adventure to life, if you know what I mean." Max wriggles his eyebrows lecherously.

"Ha ha ha," Urmund laughs, but his laughter sounds forced. "Ain't that funny, Belo?"

"Yeah, funny. All right, all right."

Suddenly, Max's eyes flood with sunlight. He blinks a few times to clear his returned vision, and then he has to laugh. Belo and Urmund are stuck in the gluebark's adhesive spell face first and are craning their heads over their shoulders to look at him. They must have run smack into the tree when Max pushed them. The pail of lepermud is at his feet. One more step forward, and he would have tripped right over it. Ugh, what a horrible pallor the stuff had. And the smell! Just like graveyard dust.

"Tch, tch, look at that!" Max says, all solicitousness for the two boys. "I'm so sorry to bash into you like that. I couldn't see where I was going. Does this belong to you?" he asks, picking up the pail by its handle. "Want a drink?"

"Never mind that stinkbug stuff. Get us loose!" Belo isn't forgetting for one moment the point of the exchange.

"Listen, Belo," Max says, grabbing hold of Belo's hair with one hand and yanking the ruffian's head back. "I'm going to go get married. When the feast is finished, and everybody has had a good time, then I'll send someone to set you free. I'm not going to let you spoil today for me. And I can't trust you not to try again. Would you prefer I shoved your ugly face into the bark, and we'll see how long you can breathe without air?"

"Lemme alone, huh?" Belo whines.

## Section 5

"Aw, it's just in fun," Urmund grumbles.

"I'm sure it is," Max agrees blithely. "Stick around, guys. I'll save you some cake."

He walks away jauntily, ignoring the yells from behind him.

*Turn to section 7.*

*Turn to section 7.*

## * 5 *

The switchback charges right for Max. Without being able to see whether Onda has reached safety, Max must fight for his life. The switchback flicks out sharp blades from its sides as it races toward him on its four little trotters, brandishing its switchblades.

As it passes him, Max leaps back and away. The blades narrowly miss his middle. He pounds after it, swinging the tire iron for the center of its back.

Quick as a wink, the switchback swaps over its head for its tail and races back toward him. Max is so surprised that he barely gets out of the way in time. The creature's back and front end revolve right around its round body as if they were only resting on its surface. That means that the monster is capable of attacking him again instantly, no matter where it was headed when it last passed him. To his chagrin, this time it scores on him, slitting his pants leg.

"Ow," Max yells, dropping the tire iron on his

boot. "Ow!" he cries again. The cut in his leg is so narrow it barely hurts yet, but Max can see blood welling out of it. He hopes the wound isn't deep, but he doesn't dare stop to check. Watching the beast's eyes to gauge its next move, Max retrieves the tire iron.

Hefting his weapon, he stands ready for the switchback's next move. Max remembers from Centaur School that switchbacks are found mostly on the mountain trails where there isn't room to turn around. In their natural habitat, switchbacks exist on every narrow length of road all the way to the top of every mountain. They've adapted their magic over Xanth's long history into a very effective offensive weapon. As the monster passes him, Max skips to one side and brings the tire iron down on its head.

The monster lets out a tremendous yawn, but it shakes its head, clearing it. Max runs backward on tiptoe, trying to stay just one step ahead of the treacherous blades. He is afraid the beast will slice his thigh muscles apart. At the last second, he bounds backward, and the switchback tears by, missing him. Max is relieved.

Unfortunately for the young man, he plunges right into the arms of a rock maple tree. Solidly striking the trunk, Max is rewarded with a cascade of rocks that fall out of the leafy crown onto his head and shoulders. He yells as he tries to shield himself from the bruising avalanche. The other trees obviously think this is a tremendously funny practical joke. There is a round of appreciative rustling of leaves for the maple's leaf rag.

Max is not amused. He has several new tende spots where the rocks struck him, and the switch back is once again coming his way. With his fre hand, Max picks up a rock and shies it at th switchblades along the beast's side. His aim good. One of the blades snaps off short. Th switchback is enraged.

"You! I'll slice you into shoelaces!" it snarls it bears down on him. "I'll use your hide for polishing cloth." Clearly, the beast's tongue is sharp as its spines. It charges at Max, who jump aside and aims his tire iron at its skull. It moving slower than before, but that doesn diminish its deadly skill.

With amazing dexterity, the switchbac switches end for end again, and Max's blow fal on the base of its shaggy gray tail. Its blades ri through the flesh of his already wounded le Max falls to his hands and knees.

Turning about again, the switchback returns t slash him across the shoulder. Groaning in ag ny, Max clutches his shoulder and falls the rest the way to the ground.

The switchback staggers off into the fores "I'm going to get some shut-eye." With a lou yawn, it trots away. Its footsteps are the la things Max hears before he sinks into uncon sciousness.

*Roll 3 D6.*

*If the total rolled is less than or equal to Max's value for Luck, turn to section 8.*

*If the total is greater, turn to section 3.*

## \* **6** \*

Max runs after them, following the sound of their cackling laughter. He's not going to let them make a mess of his wedding day! Luckily for him, the enchanted paths normally maintain themselves free of bumps or pits. Even now, the hole that Urmund dug to trip him up will be filling itself in.

They really mean it about the lepermud, too. He can smell the graveyard odor. Sometimes Max believes the old tale that the smell attracts zombies, though none have ever been seen around the village.

Ahead of him, the running footsteps have come to a stop. Max knows that they have seen him coming, but he is too angry to stop.

"Hey, Maxie, try this!" Max hears a loud swishing sound, which was probably the lepermud being flung. He throws himself to one side.

The cascade sloshes his right arm and ear. Damn! His clothes are ruined now. If he doesn't get to a dry-cleaning plant soon, the embroideries

will be bleached off on that side, and there's n
time to find Liza to redo them. But mor
immediately, he's got to catch Belo and mak
him reverse his blindness spell, or Max will hav
trouble getting to the wedding. Max is bigger an
stronger than either of these two bullies. In fac
he's one of the biggest men in the village. All h
has to do is get his hands on them, and they'
comply. He can hear where they are.

*Roll 3 D6.*

*If the total rolled is less than or equal to Max'
value for Dexterity, turn to section 9.*

*If greater, turn to section 2.*

* **7** *

Max quickly makes his way to the dry-cleanin
plant. "Hurry, please," he implores it, as h
shakes out his wet clothes onto the sharp
smelling fronds. As worse luck would have it, jus
as he has his pants off and the plant is working it
magic on them, his mother comes by with hi
Aunt Harti. Max moves so his lower half i
concealed behind the shrub.

"Oh, there you are, dear. You'd better hurry
Everyone else is in the town square. They'r
ready to begin." His mother beams. "Oh, m

baby, I'm so proud of you. You're the picture of health. I'm glad you've been taking care of yourself, even living alone like that. But you won't be alone any more. Onda is such a fine girl. We're very happy you and she love each other." She moves forward to kiss him.

"Uh, no, mother," Max thinks quickly and babbles out the first thing he thinks of. "It's bad luck to kiss the groom before the bride does."

"Of course, dear," his mother nods, leading his old aunt away. "I'm glad you remembered that. Don't be late." Whew!

In just a few moments, the plant has finished its work, and Max thanks it. His clothes are clean and whole again. Hastening to dress, he hurries the rest of the way into the town square.

His finery restored, Max feels very natty. When he sees his bride, who is waiting for him under a tree in the town square, his face lights up. Then, instead of nats, he feels butterflies in his stomach. Big ones. Big ones having an aerial battle with gas jets. With the utmost of self-control, he extinguishes the magic lantern and goes to meet Onda.

Onda is wearing a halo of angelica that hovers above her softly coiffed red hair on little wings and a veil of lace spun by local lace-wing flies. Two delicate blue lady's-slippers picked fresh from Onda's own plant adorn her tiny feet. Her dress is a new one of orange blossoms that just miss clashing with her hair, but the color is traditional for brides, so she must put up with the effect. The lacewings have also made a fine collar that is clasped around her slender neck with a pin-feather from a pin-tail duck.

Together, they walk up the aisle between the rows of guests and stand together on a patch of lovegrass under a bower of sweetly scented rosewood. Normally, lovegrass would have the effect of sending whomever touched it into fits of passion, but this has been specially spelled by one of the village elders, Mor, who possesses the ability to reduce the effects of any magic. In its present state, all the lovegrass does is to intensify the lovers' feelings for one another. Not that those feelings need intensification. Max feels himself growing hot under the collar just looking at Onda as he waits impatiently for the Bluebird of Happiness to appear.

Brunswick Bluebird, the South Village's own conveyor of happiness, has not yet arrived, and the guests are beginning to shift from foot to foot impatiently, some eyeing the tables of delicacies intended for the feast that will follow. Max quits gazing into Onda's big blue eyes and looks around.

"Where *is* Brun?"

Max's Uncle Buster stands with the book of Sample Marriage Ceremonies before him open to the page that he and Max and Onda have chosen. As senior village elder, it is his responsibility, but also avowed privilege, to marry willing couples. He smiles benignly at the bride and groom, trying to allay their impatience. "He should be here any time, you know, full of the old bejoyful. It's not so long since I stood there where you stand now," he says, nodding so that the contraption of wire and glass balanced on his forehead glints in the morning sun. "My beloved wife and I renew our vows every so often, because it was so much fun the first time! Why, I remember . . ."

"Enough!" Siegfried, Onda's father snaps out. "Buster, read the ceremony. If Brun is late, he's late. He'll do his part when he gets here."

"Very well." Buster lowers his contraption onto his nose. It is a magic device which makes the print that Buster focuses on large enough for him to read, instead of forcing him to squint and make a spectacle of himself. "Dearly beloved, we are gathered here. . . ."

The familiar words drone out. Max is so nervous, he can hardly look at Onda, but he risks a peep out of the corner of his eye. She is blushing, and her lips are pressed together to keep them from trembling. Max smiles. She's as nervous as he is, he realizes, and he squeezes her hand. She squeezes back, timidly beaming at him under her veil.

"Max, place the ring on her finger and say these words: I take you, to be my wife, to love and to cherish, etcetera, etcetera, 'til death us do part."

Max repeats the vow, complete to every etcetera, and slips the tiny ring onto her finger. It reverberates with a silvery middle G, just as his rings with a mellow middle C when she puts it on his finger a moment later. Now they are joined in perfect harmony.

Buster reaches the end of the page and waits, holding the couple's joined hands in one of his own.

"What are you waiting for?" Siegfried bellows. "Finish!"

"I can't," Buster explains. "It's time for the Bluebird's blessing."

As if on cue, a bird flutters down and perches on the heap of hands. It is a pale bird. In fact, its feathers seem to be devoid of any color whatsoever. Wanly fluttering its wings for balance, it turns to the assembled villagers and lets out a tremendous sigh.

"I'm so unhappy!"

"Brun? Brun, is that you?" Buster asks, regaining his wits before anyone else. He lets go of Max and Onda and gathers up the little bird.

"Yes," the bird says, in a voice that sounds like a funeral bell. "I'm here at last. Sorry I'm late."

And instantly, everyone else is sorry, too. A couple of Max's aunts seated in the front row who were crying for joy are now just plain crying.

"What happened to your feathers?" Max asks, remembering Urmund's attempt with the leper-mud.

"Well, when I'm happy, I'm blue; but when I'm sad, I'm not."

"What happened to you, Brun?" Onda says, taking the bird out of Buster's hands and stroking him gently. Onda's touch would restore anybody's good humor. Except those of her frustrated guests who have left their seats and are eating the feast buffet.

"I went to meet my lady love-bird, Beryl, the Bluebird of Happiness of the Magic-Dust Village, as we always do once in a blue moon," Brun says, his color coming back ever so faintly as Onda pets him. "When the moon is made of blue cheese for a change instead of green. She's got a busy life with all the weddings and parties they have there! We meet in the Plain of Grasses and spend the whole moon together, raising our nestlings and all the lovey-dove things. After the moon has set, I return to my duties, and she goes back to hers. Well, this time, when we were making out arrangements, she sent me a message that said she was being harassed by mysterious apparitions."

"What kind of apparitions?" Max asks. As an animal doctor, he is familiar with symptoms like Brun's: deep depression. He is busy cutting blueberries and blue cheese into small, bird-size pieces. "Here, try some of these."

Brun gulps a few bites, and a little more color suffuses his feathers. "Thank you. I don't know. Mysterious ones. All I know is that I waited in our trysting place all this time, and she never came."

"Perhaps," Onda suggests gently, "she has found another handsome male Bluebird."

"Oh, no," Brun protests. "She's true blue. And she would have let me know if she was delayed. I think she was prevented from coming. I waited as long as I could, then I had to come up here for you. I'm so sorry to say this, but I'm too miserable to bless your wedding."

Max lets out a tremendous sigh. "Did you see any of these apparitions she mentioned while you were waiting?"

"No. I'm going right to Good Magician Humfrey's castle now. I will plead with him to find her for me right away. She could be in deadly danger! I'll gladly pay him a year's service to rescue my Beryl. But if I don't find out what happened to her soon, I'll die of unhappiness."

The young couple's eyes meet over the bird's little head. With a Bluebird of Happiness, such a threat is possible. He *could* die of misery.

"I'd rather spend my last days searching for her," Brun finishes and reaches for another chunk of blue cheese.

Normally, Brun is able to create a joyous mood—he's the perfect party animal—but his ability is dampened by his own misery.

His story particularly affects Max, who, though disappointed that Brun is not in the mood to perform, feels sorry for the little bird. He doesn't want to remain half-married like this for long. He was counting on the Bluebird to bless their marriage today, as he did their first meeting and their courtship.

"Can't you muster just a little happiness, so we can finish the wedding?" Max asks hopefully.

"I'll try," Brun says. Max can see by the look on the Bluebird's face that it is an effort to do so, but he tries until he turns blue in the face. Waves of happiness spread outward from his little feathery body like ripples in a pool. Max can feel his mood lifting. The flowers turn their faces toward them, and people are smiling.

"Quick, Uncle Buster," Max implores the elder.

"By the authority vested in me by the King of Xanth . . ." Buster intones, but it is too late. By the time he reaches the next passage, the effect is fading, and the wedding guests are long-faced and sad again.

"You see?" Brun says. "I'm sorry."

"Is the bird sick?" a village matron asks anxiously. "My son is getting married next week! You're a doctor, Max. Cure him. Borbert must have a properly official wedding."

"I'll do my best," Max assures her, and turns back to the unhappy Bluebird. "Did you try her village? Perhaps she had another assignment to take care of."

"No. I came right back here. I'm so worried. Beryl would have sent me a message if she is all right. I'm sure she's in danger! There were rumors among the forest animals of . . . ghosts. Now, usually they're no threat, but the animals said that these moved from one place to another."

"That's ridiculous," Onda says. "Ghosts stay in the place where their bones lie."

"Maybe their bones were pulverized," Max reasons. "And they took a powder and blew. You know what the winds are like down there. Well, we must help him. Brun," Max turns to the Bluebird, who is now a pale sky blue, "I'll go with you and find out what happened to Beryl. You've always been a friend to our village. It's the least I can do, since I won't be getting married today." Max rose to his feet with Brun perching on one of his fingers.

"No!" Onda protests, stopping him. "Brun, *we'll* go with you. Where Max goes, I go."

"But we're not fully married yet."

"I don't care," Onda declares. "I don't want to be apart from you. If you fail, we'll never be able to get married, so I intend to help. I'll stay with you no matter where you go." Onda blushes. "Within the bounds of propriety, of course."

"Of course," Max agrees, happily. He loves her so much, and he is glad they won't be parted. "But how are we going to get down to the Magic-Dust Village?"

"Oh, Uncle Buster can take us in his hot air balloon."

"Certainly, certainly, children!" Buster beams. "Anything to further the cause of love."

Onda slips away to pack a basket of necessities for their trip. Max stays to announce their quest to the assembled wedding guests.

"Good idea," applauds Max's father, Lyman, whose talent is twosight, only half as accurate as foresight, but it serves him well enough. "I can see that you might need help. Take this with you." He hands Max a small metal box. "It contains a fast overland snail that will carry a message back to us as soon as you're ready to return, or if something goes wrong. Don't open the box unless you have the message ready. He moves very quickly."

"Thank you, father," Max says, shaking his hand. "Take good care of my patients."

"I will, son."

"Oh, thank you, Lyman," Onda says, standing on her toes and kissing him sweetly on the cheek.

"Be careful, my dear, and come back safely. You, too, son," he cautions Max.

Max makes other preparations as well. There's little need for weapons in the peaceful South Village, so a couple of former Mundane soldiers who came into Xanth with the Last Wave lend Max two items of powerful offensive magic that they picked up in bygone years. Old Ed has a device which he was given by a man who magically adapted tools.

## Section 7

"It's called a tire iron, boy. Not like the ones used at home in Mundania, but you whomp your opponent like this"—he demonstrates for Max —"and he gets tired real quick." Max thank him.

Old Ed's crony, Big Leo, brings Max a sickle. Max now takes it out of its sheath to admire it. Its shape is just like that of a real sickle, but it is made of shining white ice, spelled to keep from melting or cracking. The icicle has a very sharp inner blade, and the point can almost draw blood from the air.

Prepared and packed, Onda and Max say their good-byes and go to find Max's Uncle Buster.

Buster's talent manifested itself while he was still an infant. One day, his mother heard him babbling, went to see him, and found the cradle empty. It was then she looked up astonished to find her baby bumping around on the ceiling and clutching a red balloon. As soon as he stopped chattering, the glistening bubble vanished, and he floated gently down into her arms.

Since his childhood, Buster sought to perfect his talent and is presently able to maintain a lengthy filibuster of hot air for his balloon, even while asleep.

Max and Onda meet him at the edge of town near his own little house. Balanced on a tripod of wrinkled crow's-feet is the half of a huge eggshell which Buster uses for carrying company when he uses his magic. "From a winged mare's nest," he beams. "Got there just after the colt had hatched, and the two of them were out taking a test flight. They had no further use for it, so I took it and some horsefeathers for padding. Just the right size to be cozy on a nice day, as this one is."

Max can't help but agree. Nervous as he is about taking such a long flight, he's glad that the weather is fine. No sign of thunderheads or themmicanes, big multiple wind-and-rain storms that sometimes menace the eastern side of Xanth during the summer. Onda comes running up with Brun perched on her shoulder. She has put on a shawl and has a covered basket with her that smells promisingly of snacks.

Carefully slinging his weapons over the outside rim of the shell, Max helps Onda in by planting both hands on either side of her tiny waist and hauling her bodily inside. Brun, now showing a pale sky blue with anticipation, hops onto the handle of Onda's basket. Once they're ready, Buster climbs in and casts off the line holding the shell down to earth. "I'm so pleased that the two of you are going to help our Bluebird. You've always been such good children, so considerate to others."

When Buster starts to talk, a narrow egg shape of multiple colors appears over their heads. As he goes on and on, the egg swells larger and larger, rounding out into a shiny, insubstantial globe like a soap bubble. ". . . we always thought you'd wind up together. Your folks knew from the moment. . . ." All at once, the sphere reaches the size of a cottage cheese cottage, and the magic ropes descend from it to the shell. With a lurch, the balloon goes up, lifting the shell basket right off the ground. Never ceasing to talk, Buster reels in the tie rope, and they're off on their flight south into the wilds of Xanth.

"I'll take you down to the Magic-Dust Village," Buster shouts over the rush of the wind as they sail along. "I think that'll be the best place for you to start." He takes a deep breath, during which the balloon dips alarmingly. With a little scream, Onda throws herself into Max's arms, and they both sit down in the bottom of the shell.

Buster's hot air balloon goes faster and higher depending on how much hot air is expended on it. He is a great talker with a loud, hearty voice and keeps up a steady stream of conversation while Max and Onda lean over the side and watch the sights of Xanth go by.

"Look, there's the milkweed patch," Onda points at a field of pink pods. "How nice. I think there's a new growth of strawberry milk." Max nods and looks for other recognizable landmarks.

The scenery begins to whip along at an astonishing rate, and very soon Max finds that all the landscape is blending together into blobs of green, brown, blue, orange, black, and yellow.

Onda passes around refreshments as the balloon carries them south. She offers around a

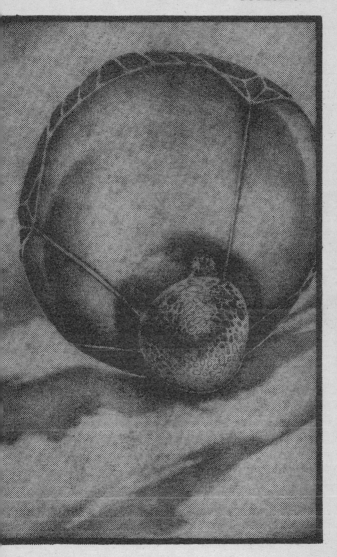

bouquet of buttercups. Max gratefully accepts a lime-flavored soda poppy and a peanut buttercup. Buster takes an apple buttercup and a milkweed pod and interrupts his monologue for quick nibbles. Brun pecks at the crumbs from the others' meals, pleading lack of appetite. Max doesn't insist, but he vows to keep an eye on the little bird's diet.

When Onda goes to replace the cloth over her basket, Max notices a square shape at the bottom.

"What's that?" he asks.

Onda blushes. "It's my Hope Chest," she tells him, pulling the little box out for him to see. "It holds wishes, hopes, dreams, and all sorts of insubstantial magic, one at a time. I thought it might come in handy. I don't have anything in it any more, since you asked me to marry you." Max smiles, and puts his arm around her shoulders. They sit and gaze into each other's eyes and forget about the journey for a while.

At last, Buster taps Max on the top of the head to get his attention. He indicates an enchanted path that loops high over treetops and down under brooks. "There it is, the road into the Magic-Dust Village. I'll have to hover next to it and let you debark fairly quickly. I'm too tired to re-create the bubble once it pops, so I'll just say my good-byes now and wish you luck."

He speaks more slowly and distinctly. In response, the balloon begins to lose velocity and sinks gradually to earth. In the distance, Max can see a village on the edge of a desolate wasteland bounded by the enchanted path. As the eggshell bumps gently against the edge of the path, Max puts a hand on the edge and vaults out. He reaches up to take the basket and his weapons and then helps Onda down. Brun flutters around their heads and settles on Max's shoulder. The three of them wave and shout their thanks to Buster.

Buster is talking faster and faster to regain altitude. As he rises high into the air, his voice begins to fade away. "So nice to see you, summon us as soon as you've found Beryl and we'll set up another wedding feast, one for you and one for the two Bluebirds I remember my first wedding day your aunt was so pretty in her lace dress of course the next year your cousin was on the way. . . ."

Max has never visited the Magic-Dust Village before, though of course he learned about it in Centaur School. His Master, Clem Centaur, was a stickler for geography. In embarrassment, Max recalls a map he made as a youngster, showing the principal features of Xanth. His effort had made the teacher laugh, which was the only good thing he can say about it. He can still feel to this day how humiliated he had been. Onda's maps were always perfect because of her talent.

"Max," Onda admonishes him, "you're glowing."

Max feels his jaw and discovers that his remembered embarrassment must have triggered his talent. He makes an effort to extinguish the light, but it won't go out. "I don't know what's wrong!"

"The magic dust," Brun explains. "Here is where it wells up from the heart of Xanth, producing raw magic which the citizens here spread throughout the land. As we get closer to the source, magic gets stronger. Beryl showed it to me." His feathers go blue in tender recall. "Under its influence we were happier than ever."

"Onda, make a map. I want to be sure that is the right village up there."

Onda holds out a dainty hand palm down. "The way to the Magic-Dust Village." Under the white skin, veins and arteries crawl. In a moment, a map has manifested itself in delicate blue and red lines. A very thick blue line obviously represents the road they are standing on, and there is a minute X in red in the center of it, just opposite the base of her thumb. "What amazing detail! It must be the magic dust's influence. We are here," Onda says, pointing to the X. "Yes, that's the place, straight ahead."

Brun goes wide-eyed, showing the bluish whites around the blue-black of his pupils. "If you can do that, can't you make a map showing where Beryl is?"

"I don't think so," Onda muses, wrinkling her brow. Max finds the effect bewitching and almost forgets to look down at her hand. "But I'll try. Beryl Bluebird," she orders. Max crosses his fingers.

The lines change and change again. "I don't think my talent is picking up anything specific," she says. "No, wait . . . here it is." To their dismay, the lines collect into a big question mark, and do not change again. "I'm sorry, Brun. It's a good idea, but she must be out of the range of my talent."

Brun sighs, and his feathers pale to white again. "It was worth a try."

As they approach the village, a pair of griffins move into the roadway, blocking their path. "Halt," one of them screams, in tolerably good human speech. "Name and purpose of visit."

"Max, Onda, and Brunswick Bluebird. We come seeking Beryl Bluebird." Max stands tall, but he is still dwarfed by the magnificence of the bull griffin.

"A Bluebird!" squawks the other one, and spreads gigantic wings. As it flies away into the heart of the village, Max can see that it is female. He assumes that they are a mated pair.

They do not wait long. Almost as soon as the griffiness disappears, a horde of villagers come running to the guard station. The male griffin wisely backs into his sentry nest out of harm's way. Max and Onda exchange glances. A female troll strides forward and sticks out a rough brown hand. For a troll, she's quite good-looking, but still an amazing sight. Nervously, Max extends his own hand, which is puny next to hers and furiously pumped.

"Greetings, stranger! We welcome you to the Magic-Dust Village. You must have come as the answer to a prayer or a wish! This is a genuine Bluebird of Happiness?" she asks, giving Brun the once over. "Though to tell you the truth, he looks more like a turtledove."

Astonished, Brun turns his head right around on his neck to look at his back. Seeing that it hasn't grown a shell, he swivels back to look at the female troll. "I assume you mean my color," Brun explains. "I come seeking my lady lovebird, Beryl."

The troll shakes her head. "We haven't seen her since the last blue moon," she says sadly. "In fact, maybe longer than that. Well, let's not stand here jawing on the step. Come on in. I am Controlla, the headwoman of this village. You're welcome. We have a dozen weddings waiting!"

Max and the others follow their hostess. The village looks like any other of Xanth, with cottages made of cheese and boxwood and tentworm webs, but there is a curious lack of overt magic going on.

"By the way, human male, why are you glowing in that fashion?"

"Oh," Max stammers, trying to make light of the situation, "It's nothing really. It makes me more visible to my friends."

"You already stand out enough, cutie." Controlla strokes Max's rather protruberant chin, and his face light goes red.

"It's his magical talent," Onda explains. She has decided she likes the female troll. In spite of her ugliness, she is very friendly. And Max seems to be nervous with her, so there's no cause for jealousy.

"We'll have to dampen that down some," the troll matron nods at Max's jaw. "If he gets any brighter, he'll blind someone."

Max explains their quest and finishes up with having to tell the eager villagers that Brun is in no condition to perform any marriages. All of the folk who live here seem to be as nice as they are varied. Even Max, a student of the diversity of creatures in Xanth, is amazed at the spread of monster types living together in harmony here. They all prove kind and sympathetic to Brun's problem.

"That's too bad," a tiny female elf frowns, not letting go of her spouse-to-be, whom she brought forward in anticipation of wedded bliss. "We've been waiting a long time, but I guess we can wait a while longer."

"That's right," says another female troll, hanging on for dear life to her troll of choice. This lady troll is introduced by the headwoman as her sister Victrolla.

Max looks around in surprise at the number of couples looking hopefully at Brun. "Our village is the same size as yours, and yet ours was one of only two weddings planned for this summer."

"Oh, we've always been the marrying kind. It's a tradition, started when my mother was head-woman," Controlla says nostalgically. "Of course, she's a widow now."

Max gulps. Troll women tended to eat their husbands. Though, if Controlla's mother kept him around long enough to produce two off-spring, she must have been pleased with him.

"A girl in this village doesn't wait if she is inclined toward a certain man. If she wants him, she says yes right away," Controlla goes on. "This place was completely empty of men for a long time, when the Gorgon lived on the other side of the lake. Our men had all been turned to stones."

"The Gorgon? The one who married Good Magician Humfrey?"

"The very one. But now that we have men to marry, our Bluebird of Happiness has disappeared."

Brun perks up at the mention of Beryl. "Do you have any idea where she's gone?"

"Sorry, but I don't. Not since she went off to the grove of the plane trees. I figured she'd be back. The funny thing is, you know, other things have gone missing, too. I don't know if there's a connection. . . ."

"Such as?" Onda asks.

"Well, you know, it's silly. My whole crop of

sad sacks, which we use for sacking up the magic dust we gather, vanished into thin air one night. A couple of my workers reported hearing strange noises off to the south of here, like . . . ghosts, or something. Funny, you know, since ghosts are insubstantial and couldn't steal my sad sacks. I ran after 'em, but when the sun came up, there was nothing on this side of the lake at all. We've had to resort to using bags from bagpipe bushes, and they're hardly big enough for our purposes. Sad, happy. I wonder if the same being took 'em."

"I think you must be right, Controlla," Max agrees. "Well, in the morning, we'll set off to the south. At least we have an idea where to start looking."

"You can't go to the south," Victrolla warns them. "Not unless you have some catnip. You'll run into catastrophe there. You'll have to go north and then west to avoid the Region of Madness. In fact, you'll have to go almost all the way to the west coast of Xanth to get to the south."

"Unless you took a plane tree," the elf maiden pipes up. "Those are to the east."

"Well, if you go that way, you watch where you're going for the time being," Controlla warns them. The headwoman sees that they are assigned comfortable quarters in the branches of a money tree. Before they settle in for the night, a sumptuous meal is served to them, consisting of very ordinary foods beautifully cooked by Victrolla over the heat of her firedog, who responds instantly to the sound of his mistress's voice, lowering or raising the heat on command.

"If you have so much magic here," Onda wonders over dragon chops and beer from a beer barrel tree, "why don't you have beef steaks and chocolate chip cookies, and all kinds of other magical foods?"

"We'd get an overload," Controlla tells her. "Look at Max if you want an example of the effects of the magic dust. I'll give him a fake beard from one of our goat-tee trees to cover his chin so you'll be able to sleep tonight."

In the morning, the travellers are given a splendid breakfast and seen on their way by the whole population of the village. "Come back soon," the elf maiden cries, looking as fetching in her working clothes as she did in her wedding dress.

"Hurry back. If you can't find your lady, please come and marry us yourself!" shouts the elf.

"You look after yourselves!" Controlla yells, waving good-bye.

"I'd make a map," Onda complains, after they have been walking north for an hour, "but I don't know what we're looking for."

"Something that is interested in stealing things and animals that make people happy or sad,"

Max muses. He feels his chin with his fingers. "We must be out of range of the village dust. My light's gone out at last."

"To me, you're as bright as you ever were," Onda says, kissing him on the cheek.

They walk for another two hours. Soon they will reach the point, a store plant, where Victrolla told them to turn off to the west to reach the plane trees. Max notices with relief that their route angles them away from the Region of Madness, the desolate plain running adjacent to the Magic-Dust Village. "Perhaps it has an antipathy to travel," he thinks. In any case, what lies ahead appears to be normal Xanth jungle. Max claps a hand on the hilt of his tire iron, sure that he can protect Onda and Brun from any dangers that dare the path.

"You know, I should have thought of the plane trees," Brun said. "We always charter one for our excursions under the blue moon. All the Birds of Happiness do it. So do the Birds of Paradise. It's a way of insuring we have a perfectly safe place to meet and . . . er . . . and no crowds. We see a lot of Xanth along the way. Beryl usually accompanies it up from the grove or meets it on the Plain of Grasses. The pilot fish call it their 'fly me to the moon' special."

"A fish in the tree tops?" Onda asks.

"Well, sure, it's a kind of flying fish. Only this kind have licenses. Fishing licenses. And of course, there's the family tree plan, for birds raising nestlings. . . ."

"Sounds nice," sighs Max. "Perhaps we should look into it ourselves."

After a short time, Onda pleads for a rest. "I'm not used to much hiking," she says apologetically. "And I don't think these shoes are best suited for long walks."

Max admires the lady's-slippers which encase her tiny feet, but he agrees that some other footgear would be more suitable for their journey. "Why don't you leave your basket here for the time being, and we'll go look for a shoe tree? Brun, would you mind watching it?"

"Not at all," the Bluebird says with increasing cheerfulness now that they are doing something about his lost lady bird. His color has been improving steadily as the hours pass. "I'll just perch here on the handle and take a nap."

The enchanted roadway twists and turns, leading them underneath a stream (to the amazement of a school of lantern fish, who glow with envy as Max employs his talent to see by) and through the heart of a hollow tree, which greets them with an echoing "hollo." Max keeps an eye out for shoe trees and good food-producing plants, for he is beginning to feel hungry. He is a big man and needs a lot of food to keep going.

As they emerge from under the bed of the brook, Max observes that the path here loops down nearly to ground level. Hopping down to the forest floor, he looks carefully around for wild beasts and then assists Onda off the path. The enchanted roads are protected from malign magic. Leaving them even for a short time can be hazardous, but his lady's comfort is at stake.

"Look," Max says, looking at a twist of the brook swirling nearby. "A water spout. We can get a drink."

"It isn't a water spout," Onda discovers as she gets closer and examines the little fountain of liquid playing high above the surface of the stream. "It's a wine spout."

"Will it be too strong for you?"

Onda tastes the sparkling liquid and shakes her head. "No. It's been well watered down."

Max takes a sip. "And good well water it is, too." Upending a buttercup, he pours the butter out on the forest floor. Max catches a cupful of wine and holds it out to Onda. She drinks her fill and passes the cup back to him.

Max finds a dogwood tree with some ripe hot dogs and picks enough for both of them. For Brun, he gathers some sesame seeds from an open sesame plant, avoiding the stalactite-like teeth depending from the top of its cavelike orifice. "A lad in my position can't afford to lose any fingers," he says, pouring the seeds into a pocket.

To season the hot dogs, Max chooses from a nearby patch of wild ard herbs, among them wouldard, mayard, shouldard and canard (which has a pleasant orangy flavor), but finally chooses mustard, because it has a more definite spicy taste than the others.

"There's a shoe tree," Onda says, clapping her hands. "My feet were just about to give out. They ache so."

"Suffer de-feet!" an ugly, gray-striped, round-bodied monster cries unsympathetically, jumping out from behind the shoe tree. Max is instantly on his guard, and reaches for the tire iron hanging from his belt.

"A switchback!" he shouts. "Onda, hide!"

SWITCHBACK
*To hit Max: 12      To be hit: 11      Hit points: 9*

*Its blades do 1 D6 points of damage.*

*Max does 1 D6 points of damage with the tire iron.*

*If Max defeats the switchback, turn to section 11.*

*If it defeats him, turn to section 5.*

## * **8** *

When Max wakes up, there is something wet and leathery smelling being trickled along his shoulder. He opens his eyes. Onda is wringing out the juice from freshly picked high-heeled shoes over his wounds. "That's the bravest thing I ever saw," she says. "I was so worried about you I couldn't even scream." She wrings out another shoe over his leg.

"This method is only effective when you're working on a shoestring," Onda tells him sternly, shaking the squeezed-out shoe at him. "But it will do until we can find a real healing spring. You were out for a long time."

"It's nothing," Max protests, rubbing the bruises on the back of his head. "I'm fine now." But he doesn't argue while he watches the wounds close up and disappear. Once his leg has been heeled, he stands up. "Would you like to pick some shoes to wear now?"

*Roll 2 D6 and return that many hit points to Max's total. At no time can he have more hit points than he started with.*

*Turn to section 10.*

## * 9 *

Max lunges forward to the sound of Belo's voice and grabs what he touches. It is a shirt, the material of which is straining against a frantic pull in the opposite direction as Belo struggles to get away.

Careful to hold his prey with his left hand, Max wiggles his muddy fingers where he thinks Belo's nose must be. The bully's voice sputters with fear.

"You wouldn't like it if I daubed you with this stuff, would you? I can't see it, so it might not even *be* lepermud. What if it's just vanishing cream? That won't hurt you, will it?" Max shoves his hand closer to the desperate sound of panting.

"It is lepermud," Belo gasps. "Please don't touch me with it. C'mon, Maxie, we're old pals."

Max hears a sound from behind him, and shoots his leg back without turning around. An *oof* tells him that Urmund, sneaking up on him to free his friend, is now sitting in the roadway.

"Reverse your spell, and I'll save the mud for the healing spring," Max offers, not loosening his grip.

"Okay. Okay!" Belo pleads.

A flash of light erupts in Max's eyes, and gradually the dancing motes of light coalesce into the frightened face of Belo and a stark white, muddy hand. The lepermud has already drained all of the color out of his skin. Any moment, it'll begin its disintegration magic on his flesh. What must his face look like?

"Gee, I'm . . . uh . . . sorry about your hand," Belo says, pulling his shirt front out of Max's grasp and backing away. Max spins around to confront the other bully, who is crab-walking away as fast as he can.

"Me, too," Urmund says. "Really sorry."

Max can choose to chase after one or the other, but time is running out.

"Get lost," he growls. "And if I see either one of you any time in the next month, I'll bury you in slime flukes." The boys flee, and Max walks away dejected. He wishes he had a more useful magical talent than a silly lantern jaw. If he could throw lightning bolts or turn invisible, he wouldn't be such a tempting target for the bullies to harass. It isn't that he is ungrateful for his talent, but it would make him happier if he had more defensive magic at his disposal. His jaw makes him a target even in the dark.

Well, enough bellyaching. This is supposed to be the happiest day of his life! Better get to the healing spring.

The pool of elixir which lies closest to the South Village is to the southwest. It has a geas on it which prevents anyone who uses its waters from telling anyone else where to find it, but the geas is a joke among those who live nearby. A villager will announce loudly, "I am going to the healing spring now!" If he's followed there, what can he do? In that way, no one actually *tells* anyone else where it is, but everyone knows.

The healing spring bubbles gaily under a cedar-chest tree, whose boxlike nuts preserve clothes against vermin. The South Village is glad to have both the spring and the tree within reach and tends them carefully.

Before Max can dip any of the water, words appear on the spring's surface. *Do you promise that you will tell no one the location of this spring, under pain of losing its benefits?*

"I promise," Max vows to uphold the hypocritical oath. He doesn't strictly mean it. One day he'll surely lead someone else there. The writing dissolves. Max strips off his waistcoat and shirt and immerses his upper half in the spring. The white mud floats away and dissolves, and Max is relieved to observe that his flesh is quickly unbleaching and filling out again.

He sits upright on the bank and shakes the water out of his hair. Before his eyes, the tips of his two last fingers grow back. Whew! If that had gone on much longer, he wouldn't have a finger left to put the wedding ring on. He'd better hurry up, or he won't have a bride to marry, either.

Gathering his soiled clothes in a plaid bag

picked from a wheezing bagpipe bush, Ma
heads toward the town's dry-cleaning plant.

*Turn to section 7.*

## * **10** *

"You must choose a pair of boots too," Ond
orders as she moves around the shoe tree, squeez
ing and prodding pairs of shoes to find ripe one
in the right size.

"Why?" Max asks, looking down at his foo
gear. "These are fine."

"They're all scuffed up and wet, too, from
walking under the water." Onda fastidiousl
avoids a pair of chukka boots that upchuc
messily down the tree trunk and points to a pai
of fine one-eyed jackboots that look the sam
upside down as right side up. "What abou
these?"

"Those are wild," Max remarks with a poke
face. "Well, they seem to be the right size." H
picks them and sits down to try them on.

"Well? Are they comfortable?" Onda asks
stepping neatly into a pair of thick brogues tha
smell of peat smoke and whiskey.

"I can't tell," Max complains ruefully. "M
foot's asleep. I dropped the tire iron on it."

As soon as they emerge from under the brook

they see Brun flapping around wildly, looking this way and that. Onda runs to him, and he lands on her wrist, much agitated.

"What happened?" she asks him. "Where's my basket?"

"It's been stolen," the Bluebird replies, distraught. "I was perched on it one moment, and the next, I was on the ground. I sleep very lightly. I don't see how anyone could have sneaked up on me, but someone did. Forgive me. I've lost your basket."

"Oh, Max," Onda cries, a tear glistening in her eye. "My Hope Chest was in that basket. We have to find it!"

"Don't worry," Max assures her. "We'll find it." He looks around for footprints or any traces of the thief. Max stops and stares and then points. "Onda, isn't that the basket over there, just where you left it?"

"Why, yes," she says, rushing over to pick it up. "Brun, it's right here. Why did you think it had been. . . ."

As Onda reaches for the handle, the basket blinks out like a popped bubble. As the travellers watch in confusion, the basket appears again behind Max's feet and then again balanced on the branch of a tree.

Max gathers himself and pounces, seeking to retrieve the basket.

"Max, no!" Onda cries out a warning. "It's a noose loop tree!"

Max hears her, but his momentum is too great
He backpedals, trying to brake himself, but iner
tia carries him right into the tree's reach. "I can'
stop!" He trips and falls over a protruding root
Long, ropy vines knotted into lariats reach fo
him. Hands flailing, he rolls over to the right
seeking to avoid their grasp.

Then, as Onda and Brun look on in horror
Max rolls to the left. The lariats withdraw, and
Max heaves himself again to his feet, running
backward toward them. "Pots t'nac I!" he cries
In a moment, he unpounces and stops beside
Onda.

"What happened?" she demands, grabbing his
arm before he can move again.

"I don't know." Max is shaken. "I . . . did
just do that backward?" White-faced, he looks a
the tree and then at his companions.

"Yes, you did," Brun answers. "How did you
do it?"

"With my help, of course." The three of them
spin. Standing behind them is a little man, hardly
bigger than an elf. He has bright blue eyes and
shiny black hair and is dressed in a crisply
pressed suit of gold and green. His chin and nose
are long and curved and seem to aim for each
other and miss just at the last moment. His
features give him the effect of a permanent
sideways grin. "My thanks for the basket. So few
people in this day remember to leave any gifts ou
for me. I do appreciate it. After all the things I do
for humankind, it's the least one can expect, but

you're so seldom grateful for my intervention. 'Let's stop fighting, for the time being.' I'm happy to mediate any discussion. 'You wear that shirt, for the time being.' I'm very flexible on styles."

"But it's my basket," Onda says, bewildered. "Who are you?"

"Why, I'm the Time Being. Whenever I was just now, I heard you say distinctly that you were leaving it for me, and I came to collect it. Only polite, you know, not to make you wait. There's so little time these days. Thank you. Good-bye."

As they watch, the basket disappears from its branch and reappears in the hands of the Time Being. The little man hefts it happily and turns to go. Max looks at the woebegone look on Onda's face and makes a decision.

*If Max attempts to seize the Time Being, turn to section 19.*

*If he attempts to reason with him, turn to section 14.*

## * 11 *

The switchback charges right at Max. Without being able to see whether Onda has reached safety, Max must fight for his life. The switchback flicks out sharp blades from its sides as it races toward him on its four feet. It attacks by running past an opponent and slicing him up with its switchblades.

As it passes him, Max leaps back and away. The blades narrowly miss his middle. Recovering, he bounds after it, swinging the tire iron at the center of its back.

Quick as a wink, the switchback swaps over its head for its tail and races back toward him. Max is so surprised that he barely gets out of the way in time. The creature's back and front end revolve right around its round body as if they were only resting on its surface. That means that the monster can attack him again quickly no matter where it is headed when it last passes him. To Max's chagrin, this time it scores on him, slitting his pants leg.

"Ow," Max yells, clutching his leg and dropping the tire iron on his foot. "Ow!" he cries again, hopping up and down. The cut in his leg is so narrow it barely hurts yet, but Max can see blood welling out of it. He hopes the wound isn't deep, but he doesn't dare stop to check. Watching the beast's eyes, Max retrieves the tire iron and hefts it.

He stands ready for the switchback's next move. Max remembers from Centaur School that switchbacks are found mostly on the mountain trails where there isn't room to turn around. In their natural habitat, switchbacks exist on every narrow length of road all the way to the top of every mountain. They've adapted their magic over Xanth's long history into a very effective offensive weapon. As the monster passes him, Max brings the tire iron down on its head and then leaps to avoid the side-mounted blades.

The next time the side facing Max changes the tail for the head, Max can see that the monster's eyes are beginning to glaze over. The tire iron's magic is working! The switchback stumbles toward him, its switchblades opening and closing threateningly, but they miss him completely. Max clouts it again and pulls himself up into the branches of a rock maple. A shower of rocks falls out of the tree. A couple of them bounce off Max, but a whole cluster of them clobber the switchback. It is staggering now.

Max leaps off the tree limb. The beast turns its head toward him, but he can tell the creature has had enough. It is almost asleep on its trotters. The blades are still as dangerous as if the creature was fully awake, so Max walks up to it and hits it once over the head lightly with his weapon. The animal lets out a tremendous yawn and falls to the ground asleep.

Panting, Max hunches over to the shoe tree and leans his back against the bole. That feels so good to him that he slides down it until he is sitting on the ground. The tire iron falls out of his hand with a thump. Max sits for a moment, watching the switchback sleep. It moves around a lot in its dreams, switching back to front and back again.

"Oh, Max, you're hurt!" Onda comes out from behind a parasol tree where she has been hiding.

## Section 12

"I was so worried about you I couldn't even scream."

Before Max can protest, she has plucked several pairs of fresh high-heeled shoes from the branches of the shoe tree, and is wringing the juice from them over his leg. "This is only effective when you're working on a shoestring," Onda tells him sternly. "But it will do until we can find a real healing spring."

"It's nothing," Max protests, but he doesn't argue when he sees the wound on his leg close up and disappear. Once his leg has been heeled, he stands up and brushes himself off. "Would you like to pick some shoes to wear now?" Max asks.

Onda chuckles. She has almost forgotten the object of their diversion.

*Roll 1 D6 and return that many hit points to Max's total. He can never have more hit points than he started with.*

*Turn to section 10.*

## * **12** *

The moment Max strikes the Time Being, the little man disappears, basket and all. Max, no longer supported by the opposite pull on the basket, tumbles over backward. He springs to his feet, brushing off his dusty dignity, and looks around for his opponent, who has blinked out of sight. He doesn't see it coming, but the next thing he knows, he gets a tremendous kick in the pants. His bottom is still sore from his escapade the day before with Urmund and Belo, so it's doubly painful.

"Yow!" he yells, and spins to confront his opponent, but the Time Being grins his crooked grin and flashes out of sight.

"Max!" Onda cries. "Help!"

Onda is in trouble! She isn't standing where Max last saw her. Following her voice, Max runs around the next curve in the path, and finds her tied to a tree with loops from the noose loop tree. Max hasn't time to free her, however, because he gets another kick in the pants. This time, the little elf stays in sight long enough to lure Max after him.

"Nah nah nah NAH nah!" the Being heckles, sticking his thumbs in his ears and wiggling his fingers. He ducks around the bole of a tree growing right up through the substance of the enchanted path. Max swoops after him, kneeling to catch him as he slips down the trunk and under the path.

As Max reaches for him, the Being blinks out of existence and back in again, right under Max's nose. "Yoicks!" he shouts, and punches Max in the eye.

Max refuses to let pain blind him. Before the

# Section 12

Being can vanish again, Max's hands shoot out and seize his wrists.

Straining with his powerful thigh muscles, Max manages to stand up, still holding the Time Being dangling and kicking in midair. The elf-creature weighs very little, but it struggles more than a tiger moth.

"You'll pay for this," the Being assures him bitterly. One of his tiny feet flies upward and socks Max solidly on the chin.

Max staggers backward, almost losing his grip. The Time Being struggles to get loose, but Max remembers in time what he is fighting for and tightens his fists though his jaw is stinging.

"Please, old chap. I'm in a hurry. I have many important appointments to keep," the elf babbles, as Max carries him to where Onda is fettered.

"Cut her free," Max orders, cocking his head toward his fiancée.

"But I already will," the Time Being says, his tone full of pity for the obtuse human. Almost as soon as he says it, the ropes around Onda fall to the ground. She steps away from the tree rubbing chafed places on her arms.

"Um, good," Max nods, trying to look as though he knew that was going to happen. "Now, that basket."

"All I want is what was coming to me," the Time Being offers. "Tell you what. If you will release me, I'll just be on my way. Not too much

f my time wasted, and not too much of yours.
)eal?"

"No deal." Max is blunt.

"Hmm." The little man purses his lips. "How
bout if I throw in the Hope Chest, and you let
ie keep the basket? It's all that I came for, really.
.nd just to show there's no hard feelings, I'll
1ake you a present of my time."

Max looks at Onda. She nods hurriedly, so he
ccepts the elf's offer and lowers him to the
round. The Hope Chest appears in Onda's arms,
nd she clutches it tightly to her.

"Excellent, excellent. Let me see," the Time
3eing consults a large pocket watch, which Max
2cognizes as a philosophical device that holds
mazing power over Mundanes. ". . . Oh, two
1inutes. That's all I can spare from my busy
chedule, as I'm temporally *ad hock*, if you get
1e joke. All this clock-and-dagger nonsense I'm
3rced to oversee. Waste of time, if you ask me.
.ny fool with a stopwatch . . . well, I don't need
) burden you with my troubles. Keep it in the
Iope Chest until you need it, otherwise it'll just
ritter itself away."

"But what will we do with it?" Max asks,
uzzled, as Onda opens the chest and an irides-
ent bubble floats into it from the Time Being's
)ocket watch.

"Well, whatever you need it for. If for any
eason you need to replay two minutes worth of
ime, you have it. Used to be I could make greater

gifts than that, but I'm running out of time." H
puts his watch back into his pocket. "Hard to g
these days, when so few real artisans are makir
time any more. Just don't waste it, is all I ask.

"We won't," Onda promises.

"Good," the little man says. "Good-bye.
Abruptly, he vanishes from sight, and does n
reappear.

*Note the "Two Minute Replay" on the characte
sheet in the section marked "Hope Chest." Yo
can carry only one item in the chest at a time.*

*Turn to section 23.*

## * 13 *

The switchback flicks out sharp blades from it
sides as it races toward him on its four hooves.
intends to slice him up with its switchblades.

As it passes him, Max leaps back and away
The blades narrowly miss his middle. He bound
after it, removing the tire iron from its place o
his belt, and prepares to deal the beast a soun
blow.

Quickly, the switchback swaps over its hea
for its tail and races back toward him. Max ha
seen it do this trick before, so he is not surprise
and is able to hop out of its way. He brings th

ire iron down on its nose. As it switches ends, he
hits it again.

The switchback is surprised that its magic has
not only not helped it slash the big human, but
caused it to run into a double whammy. It stops
in its tracks to think and lets out a wide-open
yawn. If only it wasn't so sleepy, it might be able
to think better!

Max is not waiting for it to come up with a
strategy. He runs around the switchback, avoiding the switchblades open on its sides, and waits
for it to lumber toward him under the rock maple
tree.

He urges the switchback on, beckoning it with
both hands toward him. He gives a cautious look
over his shoulder—he doesn't want to run into
the rock maple and spring his little trap himself.

Snorting, the gray-furred monster stops and
paws the ground again. Its beady eyes are beginning to glaze over with weariness. Max blesses
Old Ed for lending him such a puissant weapon.
He stands crouched, ready to spring as the
switchback starts toward him, its glistening
blades leveled at his kneecaps.

"Andale!" he shouts, leaping to one side. It was
a Mundane term that one of the old soldiers had
taught him to say when something charged him.
The switchback obligingly runs at him full tilt
and smacks right into the trunk of the rock maple
tree. It sits down and watches the circle of little
birds that appear and sing around its head.

Ow! Max has not moved far enough to avoid the full barrage of rocks falling out of the crown of the maple. He puts up his arms to protect himself. The fall doesn't last long. When it ends, Max walks over and thumps the switchback's hard skull one more time with the tire iron. Its front feet give way, and it sags to the ground, snoring loudly. Max sags with relief, accidentally letting go of the tire iron.

"Yeow!" he cries, as it lands on his foot, which goes numb. "I can't believe I did that again!"

Onda emerges from the branches of the parasol tree and picks several pairs of high-heeled shoes.

"He's hurt," Brun says. "Is it serious?"

"No," Max shakes his head and discovers that doing so hurts. He aims a wan smile at Onda.

"Sit down," she says. "You're too tall for me to treat your head unless you do."

Max obligingly sits in the middle of the glade and sniffs the leathery fragrance as Onda wrings out the heels over his bruises. She is not as gentle as she was the first time, and Max wonders what is wrong.

"What was that you said when you were fighting the switchback?" Onda demands in answer to his query.

"Oh, you mean 'andale'? It's a Mundane word one of the soldiers taught me, meaning 'here comes the bull.' Why?"

"Oh," Onda echoes, her touch becoming tender once again. "I just wondered."

Once Max is heeled, the two humans go over to ne shoe tree and pick the same shoes as before. Max's foot is asleep again because of his accident vith the tire iron, but he knows the jackboots will rove to be a good fit. They take their time eating inch under the trees until his foot wakes up rom its nap.

Since it is early for the second time that day, hey take advantage of the day to cover as much istance as they can before dark. To their relief, hey don't see the Time Being again. The Hope Chest turns up in the middle of the road half an our's walk farther on.

In a short while, they pass a basket tree. Onda icks a new one, larger and stronger than the one he lost, and they load the supplies into it.

"Oh, look, Max," Onda says, pointing off to he side of the path. "A pie tree! Let's pick some. Ve can leave the basket here. . . ." She claps a lainty hand over her mouth, and her eyes meet Max's.

His are dancing with merriment as he holds ut his hands to her. "I'll carry that for you, )nda," he says gallantly.

*Turn to section 23.*

# * **14** *

"Wait, please," Max calls to him. The little ma[n]
keeps moving away, now faster, now slower, as [if]
time doesn't run at a regular rate for him. "Just [a]
moment."

The Being looks back at them over his shou[l]-
der. "A moment? What makes you think I hav[e]
that much time to spend on you? I've got to g[o]
reset the Century Plant. It's two years fast!" H[e]
keeps walking and shortly vanishes.

"Please," Onda begs. "All I want is my Hop[e]
Chest back!"

The little man reappears. "Hello. Did I hea[r]
you had something here for the Time Being. Ma[y]
I introduce myself?" He sketches a quick littl[e]
bow. "I'm here to pick up my gift."

"Oh, good, you came back." Onda rushes t[o]
him and sinks to the ground so her eyes are on [a]
level with his. "Please, please give me back m[y]
Hope Chest?"

The Time Being takes her hands in his tin[y]
ones and pats them. "But my dear young lady, [I]
haven't got it. I've only just arrived." He look[s]
around, glances at Max. "Nothing here for th[e]
Time Being? Perhaps I'm too early. Or too late.["]
He grins, making his jaws look more lopside[d]
than ever. "That's the curse of my professio[n.]
Good-bye!"

Tipping his hat to them, he fades again into thin air. Onda picks herself up and rushes to Max's arms. He enfolds her and lets her cry.

"That chest belonged to my great-grandmother," Onda sobs, dabbing at her eyes with her handkerchoo, a white square with delicate cloth hands that wipe away her tears. "She passed it to her daughter, who gave it to my mother, who gave it to me. I wanted to give it to *our* daughter."

Max, who hasn't yet thought about daughters, let alone ones who need Hope Chests, just holds her close.

"Excuse me," a little voice inquires from behind them. "Did you say something about a Hope Chest?"

"Why, yes," Max says smoothly. "We wanted you to have the basket, but Onda forgot to take her Hope Chest out of it first. Will you please give it back?" He smiles winningly at the Time Being, whose brows draw together over the bridge of his nose.

*Roll 3 D6.*

*If the total rolled is less than or equal to Max's value for Charisma, turn to section 22.*

*If the total is greater, turn to section 24.*

# * **15** *

"Oops," Max says as soon as he emits the curs[e]
He hopes the burrs don't notice that he me[n]
tioned itch mud before in another, and he think[s]
much better curse. Ow! Some of the burrs d[ig]
deeper into his skin. "I guess you miserable litt[le]
urchins paid attention, huh?" The fabric of h[is]
shirt tears as he tries to pull free of the burr plan[t.]

Two of the curse burrs fell off when he calle[d]
them miserable little urchins. Evidently, the[y]
think that curse counted. Max shrugs. He hate[s]
curse burrs. His clothes are ruined, and now h[e]
has to think up some more clever curses to g[et]
through the field. Onda is already out of sight i[n]
the high weeds. He can hear the piping voice [of]
her darning egg and the rustle of her cloth[es]
getting farther and farther ahead.

*Remove 2 hit points from his total.*

*If Max's hit points are now at 0, turn to section 2[0.]*

*If he still has hit points, turn to section 26.*

## * **16** *

The switchback flicks out sharp blades from its sides as it races toward Max on its four hooves. It intends to slice him up with its switchblades.

As it passes him, Max leaps back and away. The blades narrowly miss his middle. Springing forward, he bounds after it, removing the tire iron from its place on his belt.

Quickly, the switchback swaps over its head for its tail and races back toward him. Max has seen it do this trick before, so he is not surprised and is able to hop out of its way. He brings the tire iron down on its nose.

The switchback *is* surprised, and swaps ends a couple of times in confusion. Max backs off and attempts to hit it again, but the switchback moves out of reach. "Wise guy, eh?" it demands sourly. "Trying the old switcheroo. Well, you won't pull that off on me."

It charges toward Max again, but pulls up short and changes ends a few feet from him. Max swings at it, missing widely. His arm is in the wrong place even for a backhanded blow as the creature reverses and charges back toward him. The switchblades along its sides rip into the muscles along the front of his thighs. With a scream, Max topples over backward.

## Section 16

Lying down, Max is in less danger from the switchblades than he is standing up. The portly animal can't bend over very well on its spindly legs to put the blades into him. Max stays as low as he can, trying to pull himself by his arms into the shelter of the rock maple tree. Maybe he can trick the creature into beaning itself against the bole again.

"Hey, Rusty," Max calls, knowing that the switchbacks pride themselves on keeping their blades shiny and neat, much as the razorback hogs do at home.

"What did you call me?"

"I don't know, Dullface. Maybe there's corrosion in your ears, too!" Max pulls himself into a sitting position and forces a grin between pain-locked teeth. If he doesn't knock the beast out soon, he'll be in too much agony to defend himself. The switchback pricks its sharp gray ears erect on its head, and swaps around to charge at him again. In spite of its alert manner, Max can see sleep beginning to glaze over its eyes. If he can just hold out until it falls asleep!

The switchback charges toward him. In mid-run, its eyes close, and it slams into the maple bark without looking. The blades on its sides snap shut as soon as its eyes do. It falls down among the roots and starts snoring, paying no attention to the rain of fist-sized rocks that pelt down on it and Max.

Max does his best to protect himself, but he is growing steadily weaker as each rock scores on him. He lets out a yell of pain when one hits him on the funny bone, and a mirthless smile stretches across his teeth as he cradles his injured arm. A pair of stones carom down the limbs of the tree and knock Max on the head, rendering him senseless. He slumps down over the quiescent switchback.

Onda tiptoes out of the parasol tree with Brun seated on her finger. "Oh, no," she says, biting on a dainty fist as she beholds Max, bloodstained and bruised under the tree. She hurries to his side and puts an ear to his chest.

"He's still breathing," she sighs thankfully.

Brun looks depressed. He knows that there is nothing they can do for Max. "What do we do now?"

Onda reaches into her skirt pocket and pulls out the little metal box. "We must send home for help."

*Turn to section 29.*

## * 17 *

The moment Max strikes the Time Being, the little man disappears, basket and all. Max, with no resistance to hold him upright, tumbles over backward. He springs to his feet, brushing off his dusty dignity, and looks around for his opponent. The road is completely empty. He doesn't see anything, but the next thing he knows he's been dealt a tremendous kick in the pants.

"Yow!" he yells, and spins to confront his opponent, but the Time Being grins his crooked grin and flashes out of sight once more.

"Max!" Onda cries. "Help!"

Onda is in trouble! Alarmed, Max runs around the next curve in the path toward her voice, and finds her tied to a tree with loops from the noose loop tree. Max hasn't time to free her, however, because he gets another kick in the pants. This time, the little elf stays in sight long enough to lure Max after him.

Max runs after him, fearing his opponent's cunning. What had he, after all? Only muscles and brains and well-honed fighting skill. What good do those do against the Time Being's ability to manipulate time? He does not want to gamble Onda's life against the value of her basket, a thing so easy to replace.

Max spots the elf just a little way ahead of him. He puts on a burst of speed. The Being slows down, looking over his shoulder at Max. He looks apprehensive.

Max bounds forward, and promptly trips over the foot of another manifestation of the Time Being. He crashes to the dust. The nearer Time Being vanishes, and the one he was chasing walks back to look down at him.

"Oh, all right." The Time Being holds a hand to help him up.

"What?" Max asks, wondering at the elf-creature's turnabout.

"You were about to surrender, weren't you?" The Time Being stands upright and plants his little hands on his hips.

"Yes . . ." Max answers in confusion, picking himself up off the roadway. He brushes the dirt off his pants. They certainly have none of the appearance of wedding splendor any more! The Time Being watches him critically.

"Well, I knew you were going to, so I went back and tripped you. I accept your surrender." He waves a hand. Things happen in rapid succession as the amazed human watches. Max does not dare imagine that they occur all at once. First, Onda comes running up the road with Brun flying after her.

"I'm free!" she cries joyfully. "The ropes just fell apart."

Next, the Hope Chest appears on the roadway, open. "There was nothing in it anyhow," the Time Being tells him, disappointed. "But I knew that. Shouldn't have wasted any time on it. I'm keeping the basket, though. Good-bye."

The third thing that happens is the disappearance of the Time Being himself. He vanishes without ceremony just as Onda reaches Max. Brun lands gracefully on the young man's shoulder. "Thank you!" Max calls into the air.

Onda bends down to retrieve her Hope Chest. "Is he gone for good?"

"I think so," Max says. "I hope so."

The little man reappears. "Hello. Did I hear you had something here for the Time Being. May I introduce myself?" He sketches a quick little bow. "I'm here to pick up my gift." He looks from one stunned face to the other. "Oh, have I been here already? Why, so I must. Good-bye!" And he is gone.

*Turn to section 23.*

*Turn to section 23.*

## ∗ **18** ∗

They press forward into the forest. The path is clear now, passing between tall hoary trees, some with beards of frost hanging from their limbs. Max feels cold and realizes that it is because his clothes are in tatters from his encounter with the curse burrs. He notices that Onda has her arms wrapped tightly around herself for warmth. He hangs his now-shabby waistcoat over her shoulders and puts his arm around her for good measure. She looks up at him gratefully.

"We've got to find something better to wear," she exclaims. "My dress is all but falling off of me."

Max eyes her with interest to see if she's serious, but a glance from her convinces him to find a solution and not add to the problem. He looks around for a shirt-tree, but there is none in sight.

Onda appeals to Brun to fly high overhead to get them something to wear. "I'll catch cold," she declares, raising the handkerchoo to her nose. One of the tiny cloth hands reaches up just in time to stop a sneeze.

Brun acquiesces. "Of course, Onda," he says. "I'm glad to be useful." He spirals high overhead, but returns to report that the only possibility closer than a good hour's walk is a clump of ragweed just ahead.

"It's better than nothing," Max declares, striding to the rag patch and stripping off his ragged shirt. He dons a torn tunic in his size that has a sleeve slit all the way from shoulder to cuff. With a strip of cloth ripped from another rag he binds the sleeve closed.

"Not too bad, if you like zombie fashions. Here, what about this one for you, Onda?" He holds out to her an intact dress in pretty shades of red.

"Oh, yes," Onda says approvingly, beginning to undo the laces of her bodice. Max gallantly turns his back, for since she isn't yet his bride, he has to be careful of her modesty. He considers it one of her most appealing features.

"You can look, you know," Onda tells his back, as if reading his thoughts. "We are half married, after all. And we've been engaged for months, too. Besides, it was my idea to come along with you. Anyone would think you don't find me attractive." Her voice becomes muffled as she pulls the dress on over her head.

Max hadn't thought about it that way before. Perhaps he was underestimating her. Hmm. If he thought his shirt was badly torn, his trousers are also letting in a draft in unfortunate places. Those cheeky little burrs! Suddenly, he hears a rip and a gasp and turns around, on guard, fearing danger. Ragweed attracts tatterdemalions, and those wild cats might consider Onda a tasty dish. There is no threat in sight. Onda has put on the dress, a patchwork knee-length gown, only to have it tear across . . . one of Onda's other most appealing features. "Oh," she cries, clutching the torn edges together, "find me something else."

Privately, Max thinks she looks very nice that way, but he soon finds a weed bearing a tatterback vest that buttons up all the way. "And you'd better keep it buttoned up," Max warns it. "That's my future wife under there!"

"Oh, Max," Onda teases him, "I love you when you're ogreish like that." Max turns a pleasant shade of red that matches her dress.

There are no pairs of trousers on any of the weeds big enough to fit Max, so he approaches a blanket bush and picks a long, narrow blanket leaf to make himself a loincloth, the sort he'd be wearing if today hadn't been his wedding day. The summer is usually too warm in Xanth for ankle-length trousers when the heat itself makes everybody break out in long pants. He is happy with his ad hoc trousseau.

A tatterdemalion does come by while they are trying on their glad rags, but Max is now prepared to deal with it. It looks like a winged cat with the head of an ant lion that got caught in a dead-wringer, a plant so closely related to the tangler that it's often mistaken for one. The raggedy puss eyes the clothes they are already wearing and lets out a ripping purr. Backing away from it, Onda emits a worried shriek. Max lures it away from Brun and Onda by holding out a fistful of ragweed and shaking the rags at the beast. He lays the clump down carefully and moves out of reach.

The lion appears to accept his offering in a favorable way, lies down on a torn jumper, buries its nose in the nubby fabric, and purrs. Its front claws work, worsening the jumper's original condition. The lion is in a state of bliss. By the time it looks up again, Onda, Brun, and Max are well on their way into the jungle.

"Are the plane trees very close?" Onda asks as they slow down to a walk.

"Oh, yes," Brun says, swooping down to her. "Just ahead. We're coming to the Crooked B-Ranch, where the herds of planes hangar out."

"Do they really fly?" Onda wants to know.

"Most of them don't," Brun admits. "Some of

them get air-syc-amore than others. The ones that fly have glossy black bark. Beryl's feathers look very striking against it. Quite beautiful."

Max is curious. He is eager to watch the jet planes take off.


"Here we are," Brun warbles, as they pass between two enormous sen-trees. The forest giants salute and lower huge limbs before them, blocking their way. "Brunswick Bluebird to see Querca," the Bluebird chirps at them.

"So this is the Crooked B-Ranch," Onda says, gazing around. Indeed, most of the trees in the area have crooked branches, and the crooked old woman who walks out from behind the bole of the oak tree seems quite at home there.

The oak is the biggest and oldest of its kind Max has ever seen. The woman is remarkable, too. She looks like a beautiful human of middle age, but her green-and-brown flecked eyes have an expression of age and wisdom. Max realizes with some surprise that she is a nymph. An aged nymph?

"So, sonny," Querca says, holding up a crooked finger for Brun to alight, "what can an old lady do for a nestling like you?"

"We're trying to find the tree that Beryl Bluebird hired out."

"Of course." The nymph strokes Brun's little head with the back of her gnarled hand. "Pretty little gal. Came in about a month ago, I remember that. I'm careful with my trees. Funny thing he pilot fish on that flight never checked back in. Well, the tree returned anyhow. That's all I mind about. Say, Brunny, your color is off. You been drinking enough blue juice?"

"It's not that. It's lovesickness," Onda says, defending her feathered friend. "Otherwise he's fine."

Querca looks the two humans over curiously, as if she's just noticed them. Brun hurries to make introductions.

"These are my friends Onda and Max. They live in the South Village."

"Pleased to make your acquaintance." She glances up suspiciously at the twisting ropes twining up and down the bodies of several trees. Obviously the ones that make the most trunk calls, Max decides. Querca continues, "I remember hearing about the founding of your village. Nice place, or so the grapevine said."

Max is dumbfounded by Querca's remark. His village is over five hundred years old, give or take a few. "You remember the founding of the village? That was a long time ago."

"Not long to me. I'm a hamadryad, sonny. I've been around since the first days of Xanth. Boy, back then, I was a real humma-dryad, let me tell you. But my oak tree is thousands of years old, and so am I." Her twiggy hair is the healthy green of the oak's leaves, streaked only here and there with the russet of autumn, but her skin has the minute striations of old bark. Up close Max notices it, but at a distance she looks like an

attractive woman of his mother's age. "I like t
stay around here with my tree. A dryad's got t
have her roots. Meantime, I look after thes
young trees who don't have any dryads to min
them." She winks at the travellers. "Stayin
around young folk keeps me young."

"Beryl is missing, Querca," Brun interrupt
her after several tries.

"Missing?" Querca frowns, and the leaves o
her tree tremble.

"We're trying to track down the last person t
see Beryl before she disappeared. Where can w
find the tree she hired?"

"It's in the back lot, near the box elders. Yo
tell me if it won't tell you what you want to know
I'll teach it how to do some plane speaking if
have to twirl it by its taproot." Querca looks s
fierce that none of them doubt she could do it
"Mind how you go. Those box elders're tricky."

Onda generates a map on the back of her hand
and the oak nymph points out their destinatio
on it. "Handy little talent you've got there,"
Querca says approvingly.

"Thank you for the information, ma'am."
Max bows to her. She returns the courtesy with
slight sway.

"Thank you, lad. Sorry, oaks are too stiff t
bow much, especially me. Hope you find the lad
bird!"

"Querca certainly does take good care of he
trees," Onda says, giving the various groves

ritical once over. Even the forest floor is swept
lean. There is a healthy looking maintenance
lade where craneberry trees and plumb trees
row in profusion between carpenter ant-hills.
Max detaches some ripe plumbs from their hang-
ng stems and he and Onda munch them as they
valk.

They hear a roaring deeper in the jungle that
hakes the leaves on the trees. "What's that?"
Max asks.

"Oh, that's just the plane trees revving up. You
an see them around the bend." Brun flies ahead,
nd the humans jog into a thicket to catch up
vith him.

"Yes," Onda cries with delight, pointing over-
ead. "There goes one now!"

Max cranes his head back as the huge tree roars
y, its taproot trailing. They can see the flying
sh piloting the plane from a safe perch near the
runk. The fish sees them waving and goggles
miably at them through safety lenses made of
yes-in-glass. As they watch, the great plane
ircles and prepares to land. A host of smaller
lying fish surge out to meet it and fly circles
round and around the tree. The pilot is rocking
n his protective cradle of fishnet, irritatedly
lapping his fins at the school to get them out of
is line of sight.

"They're violating his airspace," Brun comments, clicking his beak disapprovingly.

The taproot angles to point downward, and the

whole tree follows it, tipping upright. The crow
is the last part of the tall, black tree to descer
out of sight below the treetops. Excited, Ond
grabs Max's hand and pulls him into the fore
after her. "I want to see that tree closer up!"

The landing field is a busy place. Flying fis
zoom overhead in formation, passing on revie
for striped sergeant majors. A buttonwood tree
festooned all over with decorative buttons th
said "Fly Xanth." Thirty or so birds of variou
kinds are perched on sedums waiting for the
flights to be announced by the trumpet vin
wound up and down the tree trunks.

Onda makes straight for the trees themselve
Carpenter ants swarm up and down the trunk
checking the bark and roots for rot and chewir
off superfluous leaves.

A big fish flies out and blocks Onda's path.
begins to bubble earnestly at her, its expostul
tions punctuated with flapping of its spread fir
as it grows threateningly in size. Onda stops an
stares at it in confusion.

"What's it saying?" she asks Brun.

"Oh, don't worry. He's in a dudgeon. He say
that that plaice is restricted only to fish an
passengers, unless accompanied by an officia
He's just carping."

"But I wasn't going to hurt anything! I ju
want to look," Onda promises. "Won't he pleas
show me around?"

## Section 18

Brun passes on the request. The puffer fi
considers the matter for a moment, fanning
gills importantly, and then loops around towa
the tree. "He says you can come with him. T
rest of us have to stay here. He doesn't want t
grunts to get the idea they can bring in guests

"They're so careful about passengers," M
says, "that it must be very costly to fly. Wha
the fare?"

"There's no fare," Brun explains. "We mere
take advantage of the tree's natural magic.
loves to fly, and we birds like to give our wings
rest once in a while."

"Oh, I see." Max's attention is drawn next
an announcement from the trumpet vine.

"Will all birds who wish to visit the Isle
Illusion please join the tree on Rootway 2. Tha
you." The message repeats. Max is surprised th
he can understand the trumpet flower, but
assumes logically that it uses a general langua
spell. He watches as half a dozen birds boar
among them a mudhen scattering droplets
mire as it scrabbles for a seat near the driver;
trumpet swan tootling merrily as the sun refle
off its brassy sides; two wood doves that land
the plane's branches with solid thuds; a starli
whose silver stars look real against its midnig
plumage; and a plump passenger pigeon, looki
puzzled and pleasantly bemused by all the goin
on.

"No mockingbirds, I'm pleased to see," Bru

comments, perching on the young man's shoulder. He and Max watch a pair of wrens loading seed into the branches for the refreshment of the passengers. "They caused so much trouble for the trees by pretending to be the pilot fish that the management has had to establish "no mocking" sections. There was an outcry and a boycott, of course, but after a while they discovered that the flights went smoother without them. Now nobody listens to the mockingbirds."

Max notices that Brun's voice is weaker than it was when he started talking. He turns his head to see what is wrong. To his shock, Brun's plumage has gone pale blue again, nearly as light as it was at the wedding.

"Brun, what's the matter?"

"I'm sorry," Brun says, ashamed. Two little blue spots of embarrassment glow under his eyes. "I thought I could keep my color up to save you worry, but I'm too weak to maintain the pretense. If we don't find Beryl soon. . . ."

Max knows what Brun is leaving unsaid. He thought they had more time, but it looks like Brun's strength will run out in another day or two. Max resolves to solve the mystery quickly and save his friend.

Onda comes running back to them, her cheeks flushed with pleasure. "The planes are wonderful! Did you see the way that one took off? Oh, I wish we could travel in one of them!"

"Why not?" Brun asks. "The threat which

captured Beryl is to the south, and we'll never cross all that unknown terrain alone."

"But first we have to find out where we're going," Max states, pounding his fist into his hand. The puffer fish swims toward them through the air at a more stately pace. "Brun, can you ask the puffer where the tree is that Beryl flew?"

"Certainly." Brun whistles and chirps at the fish, who changes sizes several times while he and the Bluebird converse. "He says that it won't help to ask the tree. They don't pay any attention to where they go. You'd have to find the pilot fish that flew it."

"But I thought Querca said that the pilot fish never came back," Onda says. "Are they sure it's the same tree, not an alder ego? How did it get back without a pilot?"

Brun passes the gist of the girl's speech back to the puffer. The fish changes not only size but color, shading from his natural tan through to deep red and to black, and back again.

"He's embarrassed to say he hadn't thought of that," the Bluebird translates. "Yes, it is the same tree. And that means that the plane must have been hi-jacked."

"I think he must be right," Max says, "but who would do that?"

"Oh, any kind of jack: jackanapes, jackstraws, jacks-in-office, jack-in-the-boxes from boxwoods and box elders, the usual ruffians."

"Elders, eh? I think we had better go and

inquire in the elder patch," Max states firmly. "Danger or no, I'm sure the clue to Beryl's recovery lies there."

The puffer burbles again, and Brun translates. "He said to be careful."

"What's so dangerous about them?" Onda wants to know. They are standing on the edge of the elder forest, well out of reach of the trees' boxy limbs. When she notices the Bluebird's condition, she berates both herself and Max for not taking greater care, and now puts herself in charge of looking after Brun. "For an animal doctor, you're a blind fool," she chides Max. Brun is perched on the rim of her basket with a handful of blueberries to eat.

Max surveys the woodland. It extends too far for them to circumnavigate easily. Immediately before him and to his right, the mature elders spread as far as he can see. It is a pleasantly shady place, in which the variously sized boxes of the trunks exist in a kind of homey lumber-room profusion. Some of them are really enormous, and Max considers asking for a sapling to bring home so he can grow an addition to their little cottage. The grove simply does not look ominous to him.

The saplings are to the left, clustered around a glistening pool with a fountain. Some of them are middle sized, but as they grow closer to the fountain, they diminish in size down to clumps of baby elders no bigger than alphabet blocks, which are juvenile learning disabilities from which most Xanth children suffer at one time or another. The edges of the pool look shallow, but who knows what kind of water bubbles within it? It could be acid. Or firewater. Or woodrue—they'd be sorry they touched that! Say, what if it was a healing spring? Max knows that elders in Mundania congregated around healing pools, especially one he'd heard about called Hand Springs. He guesses that it's called that because they feel so good after being healed that they do cartwheels.

Well, Querca didn't give them a warning about the elder trees for nothing. "Well, where shall we look for the Jack?" Max asks, gazing at the expansive forest.

*If they decide to question the younger trees, turn to section 27.*

*If they decide to go to the grove, turn to section 31.*

## * **19** *

"Hold it right there," Max orders, jumping forward and grabbing the little man before he can move again. "That's Onda's basket, and she wants it back!"

"It's mine," the elf-man insists. "Let go. I must hurry away! I have things to do."

Max grimly tugs at his side of the basket, and he and the Time Being eye each other over it. The little man grins his lopsided smile. Max fears that the creature is going to vanish, taking the basket with him, so he reaches across the basket and swings at the pointed jaw.

## TIME BEING

*To hit Max: 12   To be hit: 14   Hit points: 12*

*His fists and feet do 1/2 D6 points worth of damage (in case of an odd number round upward to the next whole.)*
*Special: If the Time Being rolls 15 or better to hit, he vanishes after striking, and Max will be unable to strike him in that round.*

*Max does 1 D6 worth of damage with his fists.*

*If Max wins, turn to section 12.*

*If he loses, turn to section 20.*

*If he chooses to surrender before he runs out of hit points, turn to section 17.*

## * **20** *

The moment Max strikes the Time Being, the little man disappears, basket and all. Max, no longer supported by the little man's opposite pull on the basket, tumbles over backward. He springs to his feet, brushing off his dusty dignity, and looks around for his opponent. He doesn't see anything, but the next thing he knows, he gets a tremendous kick in the pants. His bottom is still sore from the debacle the day before with Urmund and Belo, so the blow is doubly painful.

"Yow!" he yells, and spins to confront his opponent, but the Time Being grins his crooked grin and flashes out of sight.

"Max!" Onda cries. "Help!"

Onda is in trouble! She is no longer standing where Max saw her last. Alarmed, Max runs around the next curve in the path toward the sound of her voice and finds her tied to a tree with loops from the noose loop tree. Max hasn't time to free her, however, because he suffers another solid kick in the pants. This time, the little elf stays in sight long enough to lure Max after him.

"Nah nah nah NAH nah!" the Being heckles, sticking his thumbs in his ears and wiggling his fingers. He ducks around the bole of a tree growing right up through the substance of the enchanted path. Max swoops after him, kneeling to catch him as he slips down the trunk and under the path.

As Max reaches for him, the Being blinks out of existence and back in again, right under Max's nose. "Yoicks!" he shouts, and punches Max in the eye.

As the man falls back, more in surprise than pain, the Time Being blinks in and out again, this time reappearing before the bound form of Onda. He surveys it critically. "Yes," he says. "That's what I'll do later."

Max, clutching his eye, rushes over to grab the little man. "Give back the Chest," he demands. The Time Being dances to the left, and Max trips over his foot and goes sailing to the ground, landing chin first. He skids a long way and falls flat.

Smiling smugly, the little elf transports himself again. This time he reappears right in front of Max, who has just hauled himself to his knees. "Oops!" he gulps, realizing his mistake.

Max is quick enough to grab for the elf before he has a chance to get away. The big human plants his big hands on the little fellow's green coat sleeves and squeezes.

"Enough!" The Time Being kicks him in the chest and springs backward out of Max's grasp. Max looks at his hands, as if refusing to believe that anything he held so tightly could get loose.

"Enough, I say!" The little man looks suddenly formidable as he plants both feet far apart and thrusts his arms toward the sky.

The next thing Max knows he and Onda and Brun are back in the forest glade near the shoe tree. The boots that he has been wearing are back in their place, unplucked, as are Onda's little slippers. Max looks down. He is wearing his old, wet boots. "It hasn't happened yet!" Gawking in disbelief, Max sees the switchback pawing the ground with one of its short be-trottered legs.

"Oh no, not again," Max cries.

"Not again what, squarejaws?" the switchback asks.

"Nothing, you ugly balloon," Max says, flapping a hand at it dismissively. He tries to catch sight of Onda, but she has already retreated into the parasol tree for safety.

"Nobody tells *me* nothing!" the switchback snarls, and prepares to charge.

*Return Max to his full complement of hit points.*

**SWITCHBACK**

*To hit Max: 13   To be hit: 10   Hit points: 9*

*Its blades do 1 D6 points of damage.*

*Max does 1 D6 points of damage with the tire iron.*

*If Max loses, turn to section 16.*

*If Max wins, turn to section 13.*

## \* **21** \*

To Max's amazement, not one curse burr falls off. Max looks down at them in dismay. The stubborn parasites cling painfully to his skin, taunting him with his lack of originality. They must have heard that one before. Max racks his brains and then realizes too late that Onda's darning egg invoked it just a little while ago. "Oh, that's where I heard it!" The whole mass of curse burrs dig painfully into his flesh, and he has to think of a whole new stream of curses to get rid of them. Cursing burrs does take it out of a man.

The magical rules governing curse burrs dictate that a person can't use the same curse over again. Succeeding burrs will only fall off if the imprecation is fresh. And some of the ones Max has used in the past are pretty fresh. Perhaps he can recall some of them. He doesn't feel too well, having his flesh torn, especially where some of the burrs are digging into the places he hurt when fighting the switchback.

"Raging storms of yellow rain drown you in sweet peas," Max says to a host of burrs sticking into his sore knee. "May a geriatric snail tell you his life story," he curses another burr. His imagination is gearing up again, but he is growing very tired. The pain is making it hard for him to concentrate. He progresses slowly forward.

*Remove 5 hit points from his total.*

*If Max's hit points are now at 0, turn to section 30.*

*If he still has hit points remaining, turn to section 26.*

* **22** *

"This thing's important to you?" the Time Being asks dubiously, pulling aside the cloth covering the basket and fingering the little box. "Looks ordinary to me. Standard stuff. In another three generations this kind'll be obsolete. I ought to know. I've been there."

"Why, yes, it is important," Max says, holding Onda's hand firmly in his and facing up to the Time Being. "It was in Onda's family for a long time, and we want it back to pass on to future generations of our family."

"Oh, I see," the Being says, stroking his pointed chin. "Well, I'm sorry to have caused you so much grief! Here's your Hope Chest, young lady, though it seems to me you've got hope enough without it." He ponders her a moment. "And quite enough chest, too."

Onda blushes crimson, but she accepts the compliment in the spirit it is rendered. She clutches the Hope Chest tightly and thanks him.

"In exchange for your kind gift, and to make up for the trouble I've inadvertently caused you," the Time Being continues, "I can give you . . ." He consults a large pocket watch, which Max recognizes as a philosophical device that holds amazing power over Mundanes. ". . . oh, two minutes. That's all I can spare from my busy schedule, as I'm temporally *ad hock*, if you get the joke. All this clock-and-dagger nonsense I'm forced to handle. Waste of time, if you ask me. Any fool with a stopwatch . . . but I mustn't trouble you with my worries. Keep it in the Hope Chest until you need it, otherwise it'll just fritter itself away."

"But what will we do with it?" Max asks, puzzled, as Onda opens the chest and an iridescent bubble floats into it from the Time Being's pocket watch.

"Well, whatever you need it for. If for any reason you need to replay two minutes worth of time, you have it. Used to be I could make greater gifts than that, but I'm running out of time." He puts his watch back into his pocket. "Hard to get these days, when so few real artisans are making time any more. Just don't waste it, is all I ask."

"We won't," Onda promises.

"Good," the little man says. "Good-bye." Abruptly, he vanishes from sight, and does not reappear.

*Note the "Two Minute Replay" on the character sheet in the section marked "Hope Chest." You can carry only one item in the chest at a time.*

*Turn to section 23.*

## * 23 *

They move on, once again with Onda's Hope Chest, which they carry in the new basket Onda picked from a basket tree. They are careful now to pick foodstuffs to put in it to replace what they lost, and Max stops by a patch of broom to pick a replacement for his lost shaving gear. Instead of a razorback blade, he'll whisk his whiskers away with a whisk broom.

This far north of the Magic-Dust Village and Lake Ogre-Chobee, the trail has a fair amount of traffic on it from the many stockades and villages south of the Gap. A prosperous-looking farmer wheels his cart by them laden with twenty-four carrots worth of gold. They stop to have a snack of fresh juice with him under a tree that bears oranges and blues and greens and purples in profusion.

"It's been a good early harvest, to be sure," the farmer tells them, discarding his orange peel and tearing back the rind of a green. "In spite of losing my gladiolus crop."

"What happened to it?" Brun asks, ceasing to peck at a blue fruit. Max and Onda lean forward. This story sounds like it has a connection to Beryl's disappearance.

"Well, I don't know. I remember the gladioli being right there as I went in for my supper. Good-looking heap of flowers, I thought. Bring joy to an old man's heart. I recall that my wife and I heard a great noise coming from that plantation, and when I ran outside, the flowers had been stripped away right down to their roots. There was a sort of flapping sound to the south, kind of like the wind rushing through the trees, only there ain't no trees to speak of for a mile south of my farm. Nothing there but miles and miles of grass. I did hear tell that one of my neighbors lost his whole planting of rue. Well, I'd best be off. It's a long way home."

With a friendly nod, he hefts the barrow and stalks away. In a moment, they can see him negotiate a fold of the path in which he is walking stolidly upside down toward the south.

"Sounds like we're after the same crook," Max says. "And they all say it's down there, in the Unknown region of Xanth. Look, there's the stone plant that Victrolla told us to look for. We turn west now."

They pass the stone plant, which has grown up in the semblance of a sober Chinese-lantern tree. It isn't yet dark enough for the lanterns to be lit, but the plant is very ornamental.

"Nice job, plant," Max compliments it as they go by.

"Thanks," it returns stonily.

They descend along the narrow pathway which leads off from the main enchanted route. It's such close quarters that they have to walk single file. Onda leads, so Max can watch over her shoulder for dangers approaching from the front and act as rearguard. The path is now level with the ground, and it's easy for other creatures to use the road. The travelers have to wait for a pair of road hogs to finish their battle for dominancy before anyone can pass them. It takes a long time, and Max is thoroughly bored with the fight by the time it ends. With a final honk of indignation, the loser speeds away, probably to find another hog to challenge.

They stop to let a file of San Quentin quails cross the road. Each bird, in its gloomy black-and-white striped plumage, drags behind it a ball and chain fastened to its starboard drumstick.

"I was framed," the last bird in line is grumbling as it makes its way across the path. "When I get my hands on the stool pigeon that squealed on me, I'm gonna pluck that doity boid clean. . . ."

The brush on both sides of the road is so thick

it nearly meets in the middle of the pathway. Max is surprised to see an enchanted road so overgrown. "Perhaps the spell needs renewing," he says, reaching around Onda to hold up a branch blocking her way.

It appears to have been raining cats and dogs some time in the last few days. There are soggy poodles everywhere. Firedogs chase screeching pole cats up one another for safety. An elegant puss-cafe, a striped cat with a rainbow coat, lay in the sun in the middle of the road, its fur smelling of herbs and cordials, ignoring the tortoise-shell cat which chases a turtle dove slowly past its ringed tail. Brun crouches down to hide in Onda's hair. He doesn't like cats.

Ahead, the path seems to be entirely grown over. There is obviously some attention being paid to the horrible conditions, Max is pleased to see. On the side of the road, a swarm of worker bees are standing around their miniature tools having a nectar break. To Max's eye, they don't appear to be making much progress, but he doesn't want to make a hasty judgment.

Brun greets the workers in a brotherly fashion and exchanges a few buzzes and chirps. "After all," he points out, "we birds and bees collaborated on the theories of reproduction centuries ago." He flutters upward and gestures ahead. "The plane grove is just up a little ways, past the field of curse burrs."

"Curse burrs!" Onda cries.

"Yes. It's quite a big field, too. Oh, I forgot," Brun admits, abashed. "You can't fly to avoid them." He climbs higher and surveys the area for some distance. "This is the only way in for miles," he says apologetically, swooping down and landing on Max's shoulder. "You must go through them or go back."

"Oh, no." Max has had run-ins with curse burrs before. They are horribly painful little balls of spines that attach themselves to clothing and skin. They can't be removed by force. The only way to be rid of a curse burr is to curse it off. Max doesn't want to use that sort of language in front of Onda for fear of shocking her and embarrassing himself. And the thought that she'll have to say things like that to shake them—!

"Well, what are you looking at me for?" Onda wonders, catching Max's odd expression. "If that's the only way to go, we'll go. I'll be all right."

"But the curses . . ."

"There are plenty of curse burrs around the East Village," Onda laughs prettily and fishes in her skirt pocket. She holds out an oval-shaped stone made of white alabaster. "I brought my darning egg."

"Oh." For a moment, Max envies her. A darning egg is what nice girls use to rid themselves of burrs. Those darned little eggs can hatch insults and imprecations faster even than Max or one of his friends can.

Brun flies above their heads and arrows toward the end of the path. "I'll meet you on the other side," he calls.

Max and Onda have no choice but to begin their trek through the burrs.

Onda moves into the field first, holding the egg out in front of her. "Your mother hates you," the egg announces as the first burr begins to catch in Onda's blouse. "May a cake never rise in your oven. May you be lonely 'til you're old and ugly. May your teeth fall out in public." To Max, the curses don't sound like much, but the egg is spouting them so fast the burrs barely have a chance to hook on before they fall to the ground stunned.

Max shrugs and plunges in behind her. The trouble with this nasty magical pest is that one always runs out of imagination before running out of burrs. With a guilty look at his fiancée, Max starts to curse his burrs off.

"Sink into the depths of everlasting itch mud, you soiled clipping from a dragon's hindclaw!" Max watches in satisfaction as four stunned burrs fall off his shirt. They hurt! He tries again. "Go get lost between today and yesterday, you excuse for curdled milk."

Only one burr evidently considers the quality of his curse worthy and falls lamely to the ground to be trodden underfoot as Max pushes forward.

Max's eyes widen as he follows the narrow passage Onda is making and beholds a double-

handful of burrs which will be impossible for
him to miss. He formulates a real ding-dong
dandy of a curse that will ring those burrs down
in one single swell foop.

*If Max decides to say, "May you fall in a puddle of
itch mud and scratch yourself to death," turn to
section 15.*

*If Max decides to say, "May you fall in love with a
clump of zombie quaking grass," turn to section
25.*

*If Max decides to say, "May your teeth fall out in
public," turn to section 21.*

* **24** *

"This thing's important to you?" the Time Being
asks dubiously, pulling aside the cloth covering
the basket and fingering the little box. "Looks
ordinary to me. Standard stuff. In another three
generations this kind'll be obsolete. I ought to
know. I've been there."

"Why, yes, it is important." Max says, holding
Onda's hand firmly in his and confronting the
Time Being. "It was in Onda's family for a long
time, and we want it back to pass on to future
generations of our family."

"Really?" The Time Being stares at them.

"How campy. How old-fashioned. Or is it new-fashioned? I never know when I am any more. Well, if that's what you want, here you go. What an uninteresting pair you are. No offense, young lady, but you're not what I imagined, when I heard you offer me a present. I came, thinking that you might be something out of the ordinary. But . . . no matter." He gives Onda back her Hope Chest and shakes hands with both of them. "Good-bye," he says abruptly, and is gone. This time, he does not come back.

*Turn to section 23.*

## * **25** *

Oooh, that is a good one. In less than a foop, so many curse burrs fall off that Max wishes that he can use that phrase again. Unfortunately, the magical rules governing curse burrs dictate that a person can't use the same curse over again. Succeeding burrs will only fall off for fresh imprecations. And some of the ones Max has used in the past are pretty fresh. Perhaps he can recall some of them. The plants down here won't have heard *that* sort of thing through the grapevine from the plants near the East Village. Grapevines are notorious gossips, but they're seldom obscene. Their whine is sour enough. Praying Onda can't hear him, he unleashes a few goodies he made up back home. The burrs fall off left and right.

Soon Max reaches the edge of the field and rejoins Onda. She has emerged relatively unharmed, but her ears and her cheeks are red with embarrassment.

"Oh, it took a long time to cross that field," Onda says, trying to regain her poise. "My egg worked all the way, and the things I had to hear! I've never had to use it so long before. Please, let's not come back this way!"

Max agrees heartily. His imagination is somewhat worn out. And his skin is full of pinpricks.

Brun swoops down to them from the air, a look of admiration on his face. "You did really well. I haven't heard such inspired language since I attended a curse-fiend wedding!"

*Turn to section 18.*

## * **26** *

"I curse you, seed of a road apple and a pincushion!" Max says. He looks up to discover that he is at the edge of the field. Nothing has ever looked as welcome as the sight of the ordinary stretch of forest before him. He begins to hope that he'll make it to a pool of healing elixir before long. With a final oath that he speaks in an undertone because of Onda's proximity, he breaks out of the shoulder-high mass of stalks.

Max rejoins Onda, and kisses her tenderly on the cheek. She has emerged relatively unharmed, but her ears and cheeks are red with embarrassment. "What's the matter?" he asks, puzzled. "Are you all right?"

"Yes, but oh, it took a long time to cross that field," Onda says, working to regain her poise. "My egg worked all the way, and the things it cracked out I had to hear! I've never had to use it so long before. Please, let's not come back this way!"

Max agrees heartily. His imagination is somewhat worn out.

Brun swoops down to them from the air, a look of admiration on his face. "You did really well. I haven't heard such inspired language since I attended a curse-fiend wedding!"

*Turn to section 18.*

* **27** *

"I think we should go to the left," Onda says, pointing to the pond. "If there is any reason we should be afraid of them, the younger elders should be much less dangerous."

"I agree," Max nods. He sets forth, walking

quietly, trying not to make any noise. Onda follows him, treading just as carefully.

"Why are we tiptoeing?" she whispers.

"I don't know," Max answers, scratching his head. "It just seems like the kind of place in which you should be quiet."

Nothing jumps out at them as they make their way through the trees toward the pool, but Max has the creepy feeling that they're being watched. "I think we're being shadowed."

Onda looks around for projected images. "I don't see any shadow boxes. You must be seeing things."

"I don't know. Isn't it curious that there are no animals at all in this glen? Not even a chipmouse or a tiger moth, or anything? Just plants and the trees."

"You're right," Onda agrees. "It's so still. I can't hear anything but the fountain. Even the wind seems to avoid this place." Onda threads her way delicately through the stands of young elder trees. Max stays close behind her.

"We're looking for Jack," Max announces loudly. "We want to speak to Jack."

"Jack?" Onda joins in. "Please come out, Jack. We promise not to harm you. All we want to do is ask you a question."

"Jack!"

"Jack!"

"Jack!" Brun calls, making it three of a kind. They look around. No response. Not even a scurry or a whisper. Their voices echo away into the distance, and the deadly stillness resumes.

Max addresses himself to a small box tree the size of Onda's Hope Chest whose lid is partway open. "Can you help us to find Jack?" he asks politely. It doesn't answer, and the top snaps decisively shut, ignoring him. "They keep the lid on things pretty tightly around here," he comments. "Let's try one of the younger ones."

"Look at these adorable little seedlings," Onda coos, moving out of the narrow path and into a clump of the tiny box plants.

"Onda, look out," Max cautions her.

As soon as she steps on their roots, the little elders begin to move. Alarmed, Max tries to steady her, but the miniature box trees become stumbling blocks. Max can only grab hold of her basket handle as he trips one way, and she trips the other.

"Eeee! Help me!"

With a splash, Onda loses her grip on the basket and falls into the pool face first. She emerges, spitting out water, and inhales for another good scream. Calling out reassurances, Max extends an arm to her, but her eyes are still full of water and she continues to yell for help. Onda's shriek seems to fold in on itself, shrinking to a baby wail. Max tries to reach her, but she is just out of range. He squats down to grab her ankle. She kicks furiously as she shrinks and her foot keeps squirting out of Max's hand as quickly as he closes it. Max fears for the worst. Is it shrinking potion? No, Onda's form is changing as he watches. She is becoming a baby!

"Oh, no," Max cries. "A Fountain of Youth!" No wonder the elders congregate here. They always frequent watering places, but he had hopes that it was a healing pool. Not something as unexpected as this! He had always believed that the Fountain of Youth was a legend, but the surprising reality is there before him.

As soon as Onda had hit the water, Max had heard a loud *POP* and hysterical braying from behind them. Max now glances back over the treetops. He sees a huge grinning face, the size of Buster's mare's egg, at the top of a neck like an accordion worm. It is laughing at Onda's misfortune. As soon as it sees Max looking at it, its expression changes to one of alarm, and it ducks down behind the trees as quickly as it popped up. Max is so surprised he hardly knows what to do first.

*Does Max run to investigate the face? Turn to section 41.*

*Does Max try to reverse the youth magic on Onda? Turn to section 32.*

*If Max has the Two Minute Replay in the Hope Chest, does he use it now? Turn to section 49.*

# * **28** *

"You'll be a vegetable for the rest of your life," he curses one of the burrs that is clinging to his sore shoulder. It drops away, and Max feels like following it on its fall to the ground. He discovers that he is weak. Those dozens of burrs have sapped what little remaining strength he has left after fighting the switchback.

Without bothering to curse any more, Max staggers to the edge of the field.

Onda can tell right away that something is wrong. She goes cold when she sees Max's clothes filled with so many burrs. His face is pale, and his eyes are half closed.

"Brun, something is wrong," Onda calls to the Bluebird who is circling about overhead. "Max, speak to me. What happened?"

Her fiancé shoves aside the last sheaf of stalks and walks unsteadily toward her. She holds out a hand to him. He reaches out to touch her. His mouth is moving, but no sound is coming out. A second before his fingertips touch hers, he collapses to the ground. Onda jumps forward and puts her wrist to the side of his throat. With a quick application of her darning egg, she rids him of the coat of burrs and feels his skin warm immediately.

"His heart is beating so fast," she says, shaking her head. "I'm afraid I'll have to send for help."

Brun whistles unhappy acceptance.

*Turn to section 29.*

## \* **29** \*

Onda releases the fast overland snail from the small box given to her by Max's father, which she has kept in her skirt pocket all this time. The little creature streaks out of sight in seconds. "Good heavens," Onda says in amazement, watching it disappear, "look at that escargot!"

Soon, Max's father and Uncle Buster sail into view in the little red balloon. Lyman looks weary, probably because Buster has been talking his ear off. At least, that is what Onda assumes, since Lyman is holding his ears tightly to his head with both hands. The balloon sets down long enough to load Max, Onda, and Brun aboard, and then soars aloft, just sweeping them out of danger.

They are carried back to the East Village to recover from their adventure. Max is the worst off. He is too ill to stay in his little cottage alone. The rescuers take him back to his parents' hut. He has to drink many awful potions prepared for him by his mother while he waits for the healing elixir to take effect. Unhappily, Onda must also go back to live with her parents.

"But we're half-married," she argues. "I want to live in my own little house."

"Don't worry," her father says. "You'll finish getting married to Max soon. We're borrowing the Gap Village's Bluebird to finish the ceremony."

Onda agrees, but she feels sorry for having failed Brun, who had faith in them.

*Max's and Onda's adventure has come to an unsuccessful conclusion. If you wish to try again and help the Bluebird of Happiness rescue his mate, turn back to section 1 and start over.*

## ∗ **30** ∗

He is not far from the edge of the field when he feels himself beginning to black out. The mass of curse burrs has hit him in tender spots that were not entirely healed after his battle with the switchback. Thinking quickly, he spouts off a few oaths to make the remaining burrs drop away because he has decided that he won't be able to fall unconscious properly until they're gone.

The last burr twitches and lets go just as Max reaches the clearing in which Onda is standing. She starts to say something to him, but he watches her face go white. Max supposes he must look pretty bad, but when he tries to reassure her, he can't pull in breath to make the words come out. His eyes close and he sinks senseless to the ground.

*Turn to section 29.*

## * **31** *

"I think we should try the grove," Onda says, pointing. "If this Jack hijacked an entire tree, it must be pretty big."

"You're right," Max agrees, taking her basket and offering her an arm. "It would have the elder knowledge. Those little ones are still working on the building blocks of learning."

They walk soft-footed between the trees, avoiding stepping on roots. As they pass farther into the grove, Max feels as though he is being watched. "Did you notice that there are no animals here? No birds or fish? Just plants and the trees."

"I noticed it," says Brun, looking around for any flying fish. His colorless feathers gleam with an unhealthy pall in the filtered light of the forest. "I wouldn't want a nest here. It's too much like a zombie graveyard. All dead, but not still."

"Shh!" Max orders suddenly. He pulls Onda down against the bole of a large elder and they crouch low. To their surprise, the tree shifts to make room for them. Max manages with an act of will not to let out more than a strangled peep of astonishment. "These trees are mobile!" he hisses. It seems to pay them no other attention, so Max orders his heart to stop trying to pound its way out of his chest. He looks for a non-moving hiding place to which they can crawl.

"Did you hear someone coming?" Brun covers his beak with one wing to muffle his voice.

Max shakes his head. "No. I think I hear the Jack. Listen."

They bend their ears in the direction Max indicates. There certainly is something over there, and it's having a wonderful time. Maniacal laughter and babbled speech ring through the trees, setting off reactions from bluebells and campanula vines which are wound around the trunks of trees here and there.

Max strains to hear. "It's telling old jokes." He wrinkles his nose. "Really bad old jokes, and carrying on like a laughing stock."

"Old jokes are all you'd hear in a place like this," Onda whispers in distaste. "There's nothing here but moldy elders."

Leaving Onda hidden, Max and Brun peer around the edge of the tree. With the unhappy Bluebird clinging to his shoulder, Max creeps forward. The hysterical laughter continues on, echoing in the silence. At last, the man can see what is making merry.

High above them, a gigantic head is rocking back and forth, crying out for pure glee. As none appears to be forthcoming from other sources, the head cracks a few more old jokes and produces its own. Max judges that the head alone is as tall as he is, and as wide as it is high. The neck is well over twenty feet long. The painted lips are stretched wide across a chalk white face made of wood. Its wrinkled neck looks like dull leather or cloth.

"Look at the size of that," Max gasps. From his studies, he knows Jack-in-the-boxes to be small serpent-like creatures. This one is enormous! It's easy to see how the plane tree had been high-jacked. This fellow is tall enough to do anything he wants to.

"I bet he's the one who bird-napped Beryl," Brun hisses, preparing to divebomb the Jack.

"No, don't," Max says. "You're so small he can easily overlook you. I'll get him to cooperate. I'll throttle his silly clothyard throat until he promises to take us to the very spot he brought Beryl."

So saying, the young man gathers himself to spring. Max waits until the Jack is yapping hilariously at the trees to his right, looking away from where Max and the others are hiding. One moment . . . another moment . . . and Max bounds out of concealment and scales up the side of the box elder toward the Jack's skinny neck.

*Roll 3 D6.*

*If the total rolled is less than or equal to Max's value for Dexterity, turn to section 35.*

*If greater, turn to section 50.*

# * **32** *

The face is gone now, and Max turns his attention to a more immediate problem: what to do about Onda? Gingerly, he reaches out to grab at the baby floating on the surface of the pool. Giggling she paddles out of reach. Max frowns. Babies are contrary creatures. If this behavior continues, he is absolutely going to reconsider ever having any.

He draws back on the bank and crosses his arms. Apparently, the water has ceased to have any effect on Onda, so there's no hurry getting her out.

Now she is catching the sparkling water playing out of the fountain in her little baby hand, ignoring him. Well, two can use that tactic. "I'm ignoring Onda. I don't like her. Naughty Onda. Bad half-wife."

The use of her name attracts the water baby's attention, she turns to look at him. He keeps his arms folded and his face averted. "Wah?" she inquires.

Max does not look at her. "Bad Onda."

"Wa-ah?" asks the baby. "WAAAAAAAAAA AHHHHHH!"

He feels sorry for the grown-up Onda, for he would never treat her like this, but he's still maintaining an air of indifference to get her out of the water. Resolutely, he pretends to study the

rees, the sky, the Bluebird, looking anywhere
ut at the pool with the wailing baby floating on
he surface. In a moment, he feels a tug at his
hoelace. He looks down. The baby has crawled
o his feet and is looking up at him with soulful
lue eyes. He bends down and hugs her and
isses her gently on the head, which thankfully is
lry. Dumping the other contents of her basket
ut onto the grass, he places her carefully in it.
he kicks and coos for joy. Max loves her after
ll! Then he turns to the pool, his arms crossed
ternly.

"How do I reverse the youth magic?" he asks
ut loud.

The fountain plays on merrily, paying no at-
ention to him. Perhaps he will think that it is
lumb and go away.

Max knows that all magic pools have some
neasure of intelligence, though not too much,
nd that they are aware of creatures who use their
enefits. Certainly the healing pond back home
nows all about its visitors.

"How do I reverse the spell?" he demands
gain.

Teasingly, the fountain spurts higher into the
ir, and the water spatters Max. He closes his
nouth tightly to avoid swallowing any of
he potion. It is behaving as babyish as Onda
vas.

"Okay," he offers, his tone growing threaten-
ng. "If you don't tell me how to fix it, I'll . . . I'll
*pollute* you."

The plume of water dropped to a trickle as if t
say, "You wouldn't."

"I sure would," Max avers. Disbelief colors th
water as the fountain springs into full play agai
"Okay," Max tells it, "don't say I didn't war
you." He reaches down for a handful of mud an
then changes his mind. The bottom of the pool i
made of the local mud. That kind of mudslingin
won't worry it a bit. Instead, he puts a hand t
the edge of his loincloth. "You sure you won't te
me? You know what I'll do if you don't? I'll—
Max waits for a moment, and then reaches fo
the fastening.

Suddenly the fountain dies away. A hast
picture limns itself on the surface of the poo
Max leans over to look at it. "Wait a minut
clear that up. I can't tell what it is—an elder tree
You're trying to tell me that an elder tree wil
cure Onda? I don't believe you." He stands u
and prepares to make good his threat.

The picture reappears, larger and more clearl
than before. An elder tree must be the solutior
The pool is so panicky about mixing its water
that it reaffirms the image of the tree. "Okay,"
Max says, stepping away from the water an
picking up the baby Onda. "But if it doesn'
work, I'll be back. A man's got to go somewhere.

The solution proves to be accurate. Max finds
small box elder the size of a steamer trunk
though there isn't any steam coming out of thi
one. He asks it nicely to age Onda back t

normal, explaining his mishap with the pool. It
flaps its lid creakily at him for acquiescence and
opens wide. He places the baby inside. In less
time than it took to youthen her, Onda is restored to her former mature magnificence.

"You were a beautiful baby," he says as he
helps her out of the trunk of the tree.

"Oh, it was frustrating being an infant again. I
was so helpless! I had adult comprehension, but I
couldn't say anything clearly. I felt like screaming." Onda frowns at him. "And you! You were
cruel not to talk to me when I was playing around
in the water. But I know why you did it, so I
forgive you. You're very clever." To prove she
means it, Onda kisses him sweetly on the lips.
There must be some potion still on her mouth,
because Max feels like a kid again. He blushes.
"Was it hard to convince the pool to give up the
secret of the antidote?" Onda asks.

"No problem at all," Max assures her, repack-
ing the basket and extending an arm to her. "It
was a whiz."

"I saw the Jack through the trees over this
way," Max says. Brun chirps agreement and flies
in the direction the young man indicates.

The face is where he assumed it would be, but
it is even larger than he thought. Onda lets out a
little gasp as they hide behind a great elder to
look at it. Max judges that the face is as tall as he
is and as wide as it is high. The neck, while not
extended as far as it was, is still some twenty feet

long. The painted lips are stretched wide acros
the chalk white face made of wood. Its wrinkle
neck looks like dull leather or cloth. And it
expression, when it beholds Max, is one of suc
den guilt. The crazy smile collapses and the eye
go wide. "Uh-oh!" it booms.

Max suddenly realizes that the elder ha
moved out of the way, and that he and the other
are in full view. He has to move quickly now o
lose his opportunity.

The neck starts to fold up into the top of a
immense box elder. Max realizes that if it man
ages to close the lid behind it, he may never figur
out what happened to Beryl Bluebird. He run
toward the Jack, but the painted face is alread
screaming orders.

"Get them!" it cries.

Max stops, dashes back, and assumes a defer
sive position in front of Onda and Brun. Thre
huge box trees are moving in toward them. H
doesn't know what the elders will do to them, bu
it can't be good.


BOX ELDERS (3)
*To hit Max: 11   To be hit: 9   Hit points: Specia
Damage: Special*

*When a box elder hits Max, he is aged twent
years. If he is hit three times, he becomes too ol
to fight.*

Max uses the tire iron to fight. If he successfully hits any box elder twice, it tires out and goes away to have a nap.

If Max wins, turn to section 39.

If Max loses, turn to section 34.

## \* **33** \*

The three trees are closing in. Max prepares to defend himself. He pulls out the tire iron and assumes a fighter's crouch. In answer, the elders hold out their limbs at angles, similar to the way Max is holding his. Max narrows his eyes. The trees have no eyes, so their preparations for the fight are complete.

"Round one!" announces a trumpet vine wound high overhead with a good view of the proceedings. "Clang!" rings a bluebell, and the action begins.

Two of the elders reach out their gnarly branches for Max, but he dodges away, keeping his face to them. Normally, he would prefer to have a tree at his back while fighting, but there's not a tree in this grove he can trust.

The trees surround him and wave their branches threateningly. The third tree has flipped its shaggy gray lid, and moves ominously closer, waiting for its two cronies to grapple Max inside. It too reaches for him, its crooked limb darting out to grab him.

Max strikes out with the tire iron, scoring a chunk of bark out of the third tree, but it hits him on its way past. Max feels suddenly tired, and is on his guard against tricks. The other two withdraw their limbs and circle again, trying to get behind him. He spins around and dances to the left, stumbling on a large root. He sits down on the ground and rolls to his left, avoiding a sweeping branch.

"Can't touch me, you smelly old things," Max taunts, hoping to make them overreach themselves and bring their branches into range of his tire iron.

The trees do have a smell like musty old shoes. Apparently they are sensitive to comments about it, for the third tree tries again, and Max ducks under its questing branch. On his way past the bole, he whangs the tire iron into its side with a great hollow boom. The elder immediately slows down. Max sees it start its branches for him again, but it is moving as if it was underwater. The tree pauses and then changes direction, moving away from Max, but ever so slowly.

Max almost cheers. The elders can only take so much tiring out. This boxing match will go to the challenger, and he has just won round one.

"Clang!" agrees the bluebell.

The other two don't even acknowledge their fellow's retirement. The gap has left Max with a maneuvering advantage. They can't box him in on four sides now, only three, the two of them against the Jack's tree. "C'mon, c'mon," he urges them, beckoning them forward as he jogs in place.

As soon as they go for him, Max leaps forward, ducking under branches as he did before. The great flat sides of the elders don't bend well, and since they can't extend their trailers all the way to the ground, Max has a safety zone near their roots.

He flattens himself down as much as he can and wriggles nearer his attackers.

When he drops down, the two great elders wave their branches wildly, as if accusing the other of hiding him. They begin to flap their lids at one another, squabbling in emphatic tree-talk. Meantime, Max has sneaked over and is scraping the bottom of the first box with his tire iron.

The tree lets out a tremendous clatter and shuts its lid with a bang. Max looks up in alarm, but he assures himself that it still can't reach him. He clouts it again and waits for the results.

A tremor travels up the length of the flat side, and emerges at the top as a huge, forest-rattling yawn. It too moves away from the scene of the conflict. Max has succeeded! The bluebell tolls out its regrets for the second loser.

"Never ask for whom the bluebell tolls," Max shouts at the last remaining elder. "It tolls fo tree." It starts for him, probably out of pique fo his pun.

He rolls toward his third victim before it ca size up what happened, and delivers severa blows to its lower expanse. In no time at all, the field is cleared, and the bluebells ring for Max the winner and new champion.

Leaving the sleeping elder, Max brandishes the tire iron and approaches the Jack tree. "Jack Come out now. Your boxers are all defeated." There's no answer. "Jack!" Max calls. "If yo don't come out by the time I count three, I'll se your tree on fire. I'll split it into jackstraws and burn it down!"

"Oh, no you won't," the booming voice say from within the box elder.

"Oh, yes, I will," Max assures it.

"Oh, very well." The lid springs open, and twenty feet of Jack springs out of the box. "You won't hurt me now, will you?" it whimpers.

"No." Max smiles. "I want your help. First you must tell me how to counteract the effects of the Fountain of Youth."

After Jack imparts his wisdom on this matter Max leaves Jack to gather some wits and run back to the Fountain of Youth and Brun.

"The baby is sleeping," Brun cautions him "She was trying hard to talk to me, but I couldn' understand her baby talk." Then he notice lder wood, a bluebell clangs. "Round one!" bellows a trumpet vine high overhead with a good view of the proceedings.

Max ducks to the left and dodges as one of the trees swipes at him with an outstretched branch. He is trapped in this square ring until and unless he can send these boxes packing. Without axe or torch his advantages are limited. He can only hope that the tire iron is effective on all living things, not just animals and people.

He strikes out at the branch that whistles past his nose, and scores a chunk of bark. The limb is swiftly withdrawn to a chorus of boos from a bamboo clump somewhere beyond the ring of trees. Max grimaces. He doesn't like bamboo. It is used to make magical fantasy fans, which when waved, make a person think he is cooler than he is. Max does not care for delusion, especially self-delusion. Obviously, he is not the forest favorite to win this fight. No matter; he must win.

Throwing himself to his knees in front of the center tree, he drives the tire iron across the gray trunk and back in a double swipe, plowing out strips of bark and exposing the wood. The tree seems to pause, flapping its lid in consternation, but then a shiver travels up the trunk from where Max struck it and emerges at the top in a colossal yawn. Slowly, much more slowly than it had been moving before, the tree withdraws from the ring, leaving its two companions to close in and catch Max.

## Section 34

The tree to the right, which Max has already
struck once, is visibly slower in its reactions. It
grabs at him, but he backs up against the Jack
elder. Undeterred, the slow tree continues to
menace Max, keeping him occupied. Too late
Max understands why.

The left-hand box tree, hitherto uninvolved in
the fight, has opened up, but its lid doesn't open
upward, rather side to side like a book. Its great
gray halves part, revealing a lightless chasm. Max
turns to push away from it, but forgets about the
right-hand tree, and runs straight into its arms.

Though he struggles, the scratchy twigs wrap
around him, and force him steadily closer to the
gaping box. He smacks the side of the open trunk
with his tire iron. It slows down somewhat, but it
advances inexorably, swallowing him up.

"No!" Onda screams from behind him. "Let
him go, you woodenheads!" Brun adds his cries
to hers.

The elders pay no attention, and the box snaps
shut on Max. The last Onda sees of him is a hand
flailing the tire iron frantically.

Boom! Max is trapped inside the box elder. It
smells inside of old socks and moss from the
underside of bridges. He sheaths the tire iron
and runs his hands along the inside, feeling for
the split, hoping to force his way out. The very
blackness unnerves him. Though damp, the

heartwood is smooth, with no splinters or rough places. A comfortable abattoir.

Lighting his lantern jaw, Max surveys his prison. It is just big enough for him to stand or sit comfortably, but not enough for him to lie down. He judges that anything up to the size of a winged deer would fit. But why do the elders capture living creatures? For that is obviously why their insides are hollow.

His light dims slightly, and he concentrates on strengthening the beam. For no reason that he can guess, he is having trouble maintaining his talent. In fact, he is growing very tired. He fears he is running out of air.

"There's the split," he says, his voice echoing. He puts one hand on either side of the seam, and grunting, pushes with all his strength, leaning inward to force it open. It won't budge. He falls back against the far wall and pants. What has happened to his muscles? His hands feel very weak. He looks at them. They are wrinkled and covered with crawly veins like worms. Max is shocked. In just a few minutes, he has been aged to elderliness!

He is no longer strong enough to get out. He must remain trapped and grow older and older until the elder feels like letting him out—if ever. At last, he has weakened so much that he must sit down against a wall to rest. His head nods a few times as he falls asleep, aged to gaffer's years.

At that moment, the elder splits open, depositing him on the grass in a heap, and moves away. It looks slightly younger, and its leaves have thickened on its branches. It has stolen Max's youth.

Frantically, Onda scrambles over to him. She has been beating on the elder walls, trying to get in to him. "Oh, Max, what did it do to you?" She stops, taken aback. Who was this gnarly, white-haired old man in Max's tunic? It couldn't be, could it?

"Box elder," Max whispers in a quavery voice. His watery eyes slide shut, and he goes back to sleep. The bamboos boo, and the bluebell clangs the end of round three.

"It's all right," Onda steels herself, looking away so Brun won't see her cry. "I've always liked older men anyway."

*Turn to section 29.*


* **35** *

Max throws himself against the box elder, reaching for the Jack. Panic-stricken, the huge spring-necked serpent collapses downward, trying to get to safety before Max can touch it.

Observing his quarry's retreat, Max scrabbles at the side of the trunk to get up before the Jack is fully back in its box. He feels frantically for a toe-hold, but his foot slips between folds of bark, finding no resistance. "Wait," he gasps at the frightened serpent. Jack continues its descent.

Max's toe finds a rough place in the bark, enabling him to get an elbow up on top of the tree. Another toe hold, higher than the other gives him the advantage, and Max fairly springs over the edge, vaulting into the opening.

It's a long fall to the bottom of the tree, but Max has the bulk of Jack's soft cloth neck to cushion him. The head sees him as it pops down inside, but it is too late. The lid is already swinging shut.

Boom! Max and the Jack are surrounded by the musty-smelling darkness. Max uses his talent, and he and the Jack survey each other by the light of his lantern jaw.

"You're going to hurt me," the Jack whimpers, drawing back as far as the confines of the box will allow it.

"No, I'm not," Max assures it. "We want your help finding Beryl Bluebird. You did bird-nap her, didn't you?" The Jack doesn't answer for a long moment, and Max draws his icicle. "Weren't you the one who high-jacked the plane tree?"

"Yes, yes, I did," Jack screeches, recoiling from the shining ice blade. "Please don't cut me. My beautiful cloth. I'll do anything you say, just don't hurt me."

Max is disgusted by its cowardice. "Will you take us to where you left her?"

"Yes, yes!"

"Good." Max taps the lid with his icicle. "Open up."

Onda and Brun are relieved to see Max emerge unhurt. "He's going to help us," Max announces, aiming a thumb at his unwilling associate. "The Jack will take us to Beryl."

The others cheer. Brun even musters a little color in his feathers for joy.

*Turn to section 44.*

## ∗ 36 ∗

"Onda!" Max shouts, inside the ring of trees. His voice sounds muffled even to his own ears. "Open the Hope Chest! Use the Two Minute Replay!"

"Are you sure?" Onda's voice comes from a long way away.

"Yes!" Max yells, looking up at his gigantic opponents. There is a frightening moment when the sky above him goes black. He fears that the trees must be closing in.

"Tuo kool, Xam!" Onda cries. "Xam!"

Suddenly, the trees move away, and Max is flung up from the ground and onto the side of the Jack elder. His chin scrabbles painfully against the bark on the way up, and his hands let go of and then clutch the top rim of the tree. The Two

inute Replay is working! "Mih teg!" the Jack
outs, just as it reappears.

Max goes flying backward, thrust by the re-
rsed momentum. When he touches the ground,
 runs backward toward the tree where Onda is
ding. He crawls feet first in her direction, with
run winging it tail-first above him. "Lyreb
ppan-drib ohw eno eht s'eh!" Brun is saying.
le's the one who bird-napped Beryl," the Blue-
rd spits out, as the two minutes come to an end.

"No, don't," Max says, stopping him. "You're
 small he can easily overlook you. I'll get him to
operate. I'll throttle his silly clothyard throat
 til he promises to take us to the very spot he
ought Beryl."

So saying, the young man gathers himself to
ring for the second time. Max waits until the
ck is yapping hilariously at the trees to his
ght. In a moment, the time will be just right. He
 grateful for the second chance, and vows not to
 il this time.

*ll 3 D6.*

*the total rolled is less than or equal to Max's
lue for Dexterity, turn to section 35.*

*it is greater, turn to section 50.*

# * **37** *

Back at the plane field, the puffer fish reacts wit explosive fury to Jack's confession of guilt abou the high-Jack. At each new revelation of theft an misdoing, it swells until it grows to such a siz that Max is sure it will pop. Alarmed, Max begs not to blow the whole thing out of proportio Soon, the fish brings itself under control agai and accedes grumpily to Max's request that th Jack be allowed to fly a plane tree to the Plain Grasses. "This wooden knave shouldn't b allowed to do anything but be pressed into card Never trust anyone whose face looks the sam upside down as right side up. Where's the pilo fish that originally flew this tree?"

"South of here," Jack confesses. "I caught hi with a sky-hook and tied him by the gills to gillyflower. He's quite safe."

"That's terrible!" Onda exclaims.

"Well, I didn't stuff him in a little basket," th Jack creels. "This way he can still graze on th treetops."

"Very well," the puffer decides. "You may tak the tree to find Beryl Bluebird, but I want brought back safely by one of my own crew. The we'll see about your punishment."

"It won't be much fun if I can't high-jack it,

e serpent mumbles, unsatisfied. "You can keep
our puns."

"Quiet," Max says out of the corner of his
mouth. "You're lucky you're not being made to
o hard labor, like clearing this field for the
lanes to land on."

"Hmmph! I'm not a Jack-ass or a Jack-hammer."

"I thought you said you could do anything,"
Max tosses off, tauntingly.

"Certainly I can. I'm a Jack-of-all-trades."

"I'll be responsible for him," Max tells the
uffer. Brun translates for him. "You can send a
eliable pilot fish with us to make sure no funny
uff goes on."

"You had better be sure nothing does," the
uffer fish relays through Brun. The tree is made
eady, and the party prepares to depart.

The plane sets out from the grove with a full
rew. A glass spider creeps down from the highest
ranches of the tree to weave fiberglass hammocks for the humans because the branches
might prove to be uncomfortable. Brun has appropriated a nice firm perch near the pilot and
ocks his claws firmly into the bark. They all sway
ard back when the plane takes off. "Smooth
de!" the puffer fish's wish bubbles after them.

"So then the guy says, "And they have this
osition open for tree fellers, but there's only two
f us. Hahahaha! Isn't that a hot one?"

## Section 37

"Quiet," Max complains, after the Jack's hun
dredth or so punch line. "The puffer let us tak
this on condition that there was no funny stuff."

"You call those antiquated kernels from
horse chestnut tree funny?" Brun asks wearily. I
anything, the Bluebird looks more bored than th
two humans. Max fears for the little bird'
strength and wishes the Jack would shut up. Th
serpent seems to have an endless supply of tre
jokes.

"Is anybody hungry?" Onda asks brightly
trying to distract them from their continue
verbal Jack-knifing. She hands around brightl
colored soda poppies and poppadoms, snapp
little hemispheric crackers from an Indian bread
fruit tree. For the Jack, Onda has popcorn, which
bursts with jokes of a more recent harvest tha
the ones he has been telling.

Instead of flying straight, the tree swoops an
dives. Clearly, it is having a terrific time, but th
ups and downs of travel are hard on Max an
Onda.

"We're not used to stunt flying," Onda ex
plains.

"I promise you," the pilot fish assures them
"this tree is not stunted. It is fully grown."

Besides all the swooping, flying proves to be
pleasant way to travel. Occasional birds fly up t
roost in the plane's limbs and to keep compan
with Brun and the pilot fish. Max is enjoying th
chatter and watching his lady trying to under
stand bird-speak without a translator.

Without warning, their plane dives sharply toward a grove of extra long banananananas in the jungle below them. The pilot fish notices how close they are to the jungle top and pulls the tree up just in time.

"What were you trying to do?" the pilot fish bubbles angrily at Jack, stabilizing the confused tree which dips and bucks until it calms down.

"I think he wanted to give us the slip," Brun frowns, communicating in fish-speak. "You could slide a long way on those banananananas. You'd never be able to stop! Meantime, he'd make his escape." Fish and bird glare at the guilty serpent, who cowers.

"What happened?" Max demands, in people-talk, alarmed at the sudden jolt and slide.

The pilot fish burbles indignantly at Max.

"The Jack tried to crash-land us," Brun translates grimly.

"Why?" Max adds his scrutiny to that of the others.

"Oh, please, don't make me fly down there again," the Jack whines, abasing itself as best a ninety-foot cloth snake can. "He'll haunt me to death if he knows I betrayed him. His spy-I spies are everywhere!"

"Who will?" Max asks, clambering along the plane's limbs and clutching the Jack-in-the-box by the cloth under its chin. "Tell me or I'll sew you in a loop!"

"The Ghost Writer. Oh, I'm so frightened."

"Who, or what, is the Ghost Writer?"

Jack has to be persuaded to talk any more. His painted teeth are chattering together. "He's a human being, like yourselves. He lives in the depths of the swamplands north of the Centaur Isle, south of the Plain of Grasses."

"No humans live down there," Max says, puzzled, recalling his geography. "There isn't a stockade or a village for miles in the south of Xanth."

"He does. I don't think he likes other people very much. It doesn't bother him to be alone. He is capturing all of the Bluebirds, uprooting constancy herbs—"

"—Sad sacks, rue, gladioli, worry worts, anything to do with emotion. We've been hearing complaints about the disappearances from other people, too," Max informs him.

"Well, you see? You don't want to mess with him. He's dangerous. He's powerful! He wants to take over all the emotions in Xanth."

"What's his talent?" Onda asks.

"I'm not sure," Jack whimpers. "But it has to do with ghosts."

"Why did you help him?"

"He said he'd haunt me the rest of my life if I didn't. He can do it, too!" Jack shivers, sending ripples all the way to his bell. "I think he makes ghosts."

"We have to save Beryl Bluebird." Max turns to Onda, who is already concentrating on formulating her magic. "Can you make a map of that area? A close-up map?"

"Unless I get lucky and strike the Ghost Writer's home the first time, I could be searching the whole expanse of South Xanth," Onda says apologetically. "My magic isn't that strong. If I had the ability of say, Chem Centaur who works at Castle Roogna, but hers is a different and more powerful map magic. I don't have to have seen the area before, but I won't necessarily know what I'm looking at. I can make educated guesses."

"That'll have to be good enough," Max says.

For a while, Max watches the cartography change on the back of Onda's hand, but he gets dizzy trying to guess what he is looking at and climbs back up to help Brun and the fish supervise Jack's navigation.

The land below them changes more dramatically than that near Lake Ogre-Chobee. Mountains underneath them climb high up, trying to catch the passing tree, and then climb down again, giving up the chase. Very few enchanted paths wander through the jungle down there. It is such wild country, they must feel too unsafe. The centaurs from the Centaur Isle off the southern coast of the Xanth peninsula use the enchanted paths only rarely, often preferring to force their way through the jungle than to knowingly employ magic. Most Centaurs of the old school consider magic obscene. Max looks at the thickness of the undergrowth and thinks that he'd rather face a little obscenity himself, but he won't judge the centaurs' principles.

# Section 37

The shadows are getting very long when a clearing surrounded by very tall trees with thick foliage appears not too far ahead.

"There it is," Jack announces. "That's the Phantom Ranch! Shall I set down near it?"

Max can't see any buildings from his vantage point. "Are you sure?"

"Positively, absolutely. Would I lie to you?" the Jack asks guilelessly.

Max shrugs. "It's getting late," he says, keenly surveying the clearing. He can't see what the Jack is afraid of, but this Ghost Writer's place may be at the close end under the shadow of the big trees. Sighing, he watches the sun retreat from the rainbow of aggressive colors pursuing it over the horizon. "Set down just outside of the clearing. Don't let him know we're here. I for one need to rest up before confronting him."

"Me, too," Onda agrees. "I wouldn't be much help unless I get some sleep."

"Yes," the Jack adds sympathetically. "I'm afraid too."

"Put a lid on it," Max snaps. "Well, I am afraid, but I mean to rescue the ladybird. I'm too tired to be of any use tonight."

"There's really no need to land at all," Brun assures them. "These are first-class accommodations. That's why Beryl and I like taking plane trees. Just lean back in your hammocks and relax. The tree won't have to set down until it gets tired, and they don't tire easily."

"That's a good idea," Onda assents, and pats a yawn daintily. She settles into her hammock with one hand under her head.

Max smiles to himself and loosens the tire iron at his belt. He curls up in his hammock and lets himself drift off to sleep. The tree hovers in mid-air all night long.

The next morning, the others wake up before Max does. The sounds and smells of breakfast preparation make him perk up his nose. In the supply hole in the trunk of the tree are scrambled eggplant, pods from milkweeds, and yesterday's breadfruit toasted over a fireweed and spread with butter from buttercups.

The pilot fish waits patiently for his breakfast to finish being prepared: a bowl of wormgrass in which he has dropped a cutworm to cut up the long wiggly strands. Onda turns away from the sight a little sickened but soon revives with the taste of fresh greenfruit and grapes from a grapefruit.

All through the meal, the Jack keeps urging them, "Hurry, hurry, hurry! You don't want him to discover you. Get out and go!" He has wrapped himself so tightly around the trunk that the tree sways in protest.

"Have patience," Max cautions him. "We don't want to charge in there unprepared." He is sharpening his icicle with a frond of fireweed. The tire iron, polished to a gleam, is ready.

# Section 37

The Jack grumbles, his painted lip curling.

Soon, Brun and the humans are ready for the attack. "Can you set down here?" Max inquires of the pilot fish, pointing down into a narrow spot. "I think there's room in there for the roots."

"Have to see what the tree says," Brun translates for the pilot. "The planes deign to land mainly in the plain."

"The planes deign to land mainly in the plain?" Max repeats unsurely.

Joyfully, the fish blows a bubble in the air. "I think he's got it!" he says to Brun. "The tree agrees."

Slowly, the great plane rights itself. Max and Onda cling to their hammocks. Onda holds her basket carefully in her lap to keep the contents from tumbling out. Taproot extended, the tree sinks down into the little hollow. It lands with a *thud*.

"Shh!" Max hisses, looking around wildly.

"That's it," Brun tells him. "It's up to us, now."

As soon as Max and the others are clear, the Jack leaps for the center perch and urges the tree to take off. "Good-bye!" he cries.

They are too busy to pay him much attention. Max signals silently to the others to stay in the low clearing where they are safe. He tiptoes up the rise, stepping over the brush, taking especial care to avoid the clumps of hair brush and wire brush, which could trip him up. In a moment he returns and whispers over the edge of the depression.

"I can't see anything through those big trees at the edge. I'm going to climb one and spy down on the Ghost Writer's clearing."

"Be careful!" Onda pleads.

Max approaches a huge specimen of a tree, one with shaggy brown bark and easy-to-reach lower limbs standing out at right angles from its sides. He keeps the tree between him and the clearing. It certainly is quiet on the Phantom Ranch. What if everyone there is a ghost? With a darting glance to make sure no one is sneaking up on him, he bounds upward and grabs for the lowest branch.

His fists curl around the thick branch, and keep closing in on themselves until they are clutching nothing. Max's astonishment prevents him from making any effort to save himself as he catapults right through the tree and falls into a hole in the ground concealed by its immaterial bulk. His cry of surprise alerts Onda and Brun, who hurry to his rescue.

Max rises to his knees. His chin and elbows are badly scraped, but nothing is broken. He finds himself in a pit which terminates in many smaller tunnels and a narrow but very deep hole in the center. Some, he can feel with a toe or a hand, are only a few inches across. He lights up his chin to take a look, but his talent seems to be stifled in here. The bright light shines up under his cheekbones, and he can see it out of the bottom of his eyes, but it doesn't dispel any of the darkness ahead of him. As he ducks further down, the beam shines out a few inches in random stripes. With a little more exploration, he realizes what he has fallen into.

"This is a tree's root system," he says to himself. "Maybe it leads into the Ranch. The Jack didn't say it was underground."

"Max?" cries Onda's voice from above him. "Where are you?"

"I'm inside the tree!" Max whispers urgently. "Be quiet. I don't want the Ghost Writer to hear you!"

Onda nervously looks around the field. "But there's no one here! This must be the wrong place. We're alone. I'm sure of it. How can we help you out?"

"Don't touch the tree. It isn't there. It's a shade tree. I fell down here when I tried to climb it."

"Shade trees," Brun's voice came. "The ghosts of real trees that died, either by fire or by deliberate vandalism and mischief. This whole field is full of them. I wonder what happened here?"

Max feels for the edge of the pit and boosts himself out.

Onda shrieks as she sees a pair of hands and then a pate of thick black fur emerging from the side of a seemingly solid tree. She picks up a fallen branch to clout it, fearing a bugbear or some worse monster. To her relief, Max's face is

under the black hair, and his arms follow his hands. "Oh, how strange," she says, offering him the branch. "Are they all like this?"

The party makes a tour of the field and discovers that all the big trees are shades of their former selves. Max pokes at each one with his improvised walking stick, and the stick passes through the bark effortlessly. And there is no one here at all.

"So it is a phantom ranch, of a sort," Max growls, throwing down the stick. "But not the one we want. Drat that Jack!"

"Well, it must look like it, or the Jack would never expect us to be fooled," Brun offers.

"Yes, I think you're right," Onda says, holding out her hand. "Look at this."

They all look at her map, which displays a broad clearing in the midst of jungle. "That's where we are," Max says, pointing.

"No," Onda corrects him, ordering her map to scroll northwards. "*This* is where we are." The back of her hand now shows an identical field. "The Phantom Ranch is still south of here, but now we know where it is!"

"How far away?"

Onda sighs. "A long way, since we have to walk it. But there's a good path." She points out a faint vein. "It's not enchanted, and there's an interruption I can't identify up ahead, but it's direct."

"We'd better start walking," Max says with resignation.

Beyond the field, the land does not appear to have had much traffic. The grass is nearly waist high among the trees and shrubs except for a narrow track on which Onda guides them. The path runs out at a body of deep green sludge that bobbles playfully at their feet.

"This is it," Onda says. "It's a mallow marsh." She pokes at it with her toe. The goo gives slightly, but some of it adheres stickily to her shoe. Disgusted, she turns away to wipe her foot on the grass.

Max kneels to dip a finger into the marshmallow. "We can eat it, but we can't cross it," he complains. "Onda, how wide is this thing?"

"Miles wide. It goes right off the side of my hand."

"Permit me? May I be of service?" A strange voice accosts them. The travelers spin around to see a handsome young man standing on the deck of a trim little feline boat.

His appearance is extraordinary, not merely for its unexpectedness, but for his physical description. He is as tall as Max and handsomely muscled, but he is of a metallic gold from hair to shoes. He wears a wide golden smile, a pair of brassards, and not much else.

"Who are you?" Onda asks timidly.

"No need to be shy, soft young lady. My name is Fortinbrass. Please, climb aboard, and I'll have the three of you across the mallow before you can say 'brassica oleracea capitata.'"

"What's that?" Max asks, letting the man hand
him aboard.

"Well, the version I've seen out here in your
soft world is called cabbage. Same leaves, only
it's missing that tasty hard texture and the
healthy color I associate with well-grown
brassica."

"We're grateful for your help, but we don't
want to make ourselves unwelcome," Onda offers shyly.

"Unwelcome?" Fortinbrass says boldly, for
that was his nature. "Why, I'm offering you the
meat o' the kitty! Please, sit down and enjoy
yourselves. I'll have you across this marsh in no
time. My pleasure." Once his guests are seated,
the man calls out, "Okay, Cat! Let's sail!"

The little boat turns away from the bank and
edges into the sweet green goo. Max introduces
himself, Onda, and Brun to the young man who
shakes hands with a brazen grip.

"You're sailing aboard my friend Cat
O'Moran. She's a fine craft lent me by the cool
cats in Lake Ogre-Chobee. I'm from the City of
the Brassies."

"Oh, inside the hypnogourd?" Max exclaims.
"What are you doing out here?"

"Having a terrific time," Fortinbrass laughs.
"Now you mustn't think I'm crazy just because
I'm out of my gourd. Me and my catamaran here
have been sailing about and seeing what there is
to see of Xanth. I'm in Centaur School at the

North Village, but I'm on vacation for a while. The school mistress is a real nag, but I like a tough teacher. The rest of this world is too soft."

He grins up at a sword fern that stabs vainly at his impenetrable skin and brushes it away. The fern, frustrated, gashes the nearest thing next to it, an ink plant, which retaliates by spraying the whole shore black. The mess annoys a tinkerbell next to it, which rings furiously, attracting the attention of the sword fern. Fortinbrass poles the boat away from the inky tink ado.

"Reminds me of the time we sailed into a patch of brooklime, and the boat stuck fast. Took us a while to get free, I'll tell you! I don't sail much in the gourd. Too hot. In my home, you always have a sky like brass. In fact, it is brass! Besides, there's no water. You can brass-skate. I'm good at that. You can cross-foundry ski. But there's nothing like sailing. I wish I could bring my catamaran home to meet the rest of my brass menagerie. I've got several animals. There's the brass ball-cock, a round birdie. There's the wire duck. Smart little fella. I have a half-broken brass horse I have to ride with a lead pipe cinch. And my dog, of course; she's a purebred brassica oleracea botrytis collie named Flower."

"Our society must be very different than yours," Max suggests, "if so little can hurt you."

"Oh, yes, it makes us brassier than you. But you handle some things better than we do, like the care of other metal beasts, for example. I've

ot a few good head of pig iron that are suffering
rom ox-idization and other unnatural metamor-
hic illnesses like that. Might spread to the rest of
ne brassica plantations one day and do away
rith brassica alba, campestris, monensis, napus
nd nigra; and I'd hate to see that happen. I need
o find a cure before they corrode away. And then
met my girl at the school. She's from out here.
Ier name's Patchricia. She is an animate rag
oll, but I like her just the way she is. My folks
re making a big fuss, say our kids'll be nothing
ut a lot of brass rags and tags, but what do they
now? I've seen some pretty strange couples
aake do out here."

"Fortinbrass," a thick brogue rolls out from
ne bow of the boat, "company coming." It is Cat
)'Moran's voice.

"Hmph! Marsh monsters. Well, we'll soon
nake short work of them! Care to assist? You
ake the ones on the right, and I'll take the ones
n the left."

Max has only time to draw the sharp white
urve of the icicle before the intruders rise out of
he sticky marsh. "Samphires!" he cries, recog-
izing the threat.

## MARSH SAMPHIRES (2)
*o hit Max: 10   To be hit: 13   Hit points: 12*

*amphires are living marshweed that have long
harp thorns through which they draw out the*

*blood of their prey. Samphires do 106+2 points of damage per hit.*

*Max does 1 D6+1 with the icicle.*

*If Max wins, turn to section 57.*

*If Max loses, turn to section 61.*

* **38** *

"What can you possibly do against them?" Onda shrieks and clutches Max's arm.

"They're elderly," Max points out. "I think they'll get tired of fighting me and go away if I hit them with this." He claps a hand to the tire iron.

The three trees are closing in. Max boosts Onda up on top of the Jack-in-the-elder-box and prepares to defend himself. "They can reach you up there, but not as easily as down here. If they try to grab you, jump off the other side!"

Grasping at twigs, Onda looks down at the drop and forms a retort to fire back at Max, but he is already engaged with the elders.

Max draws the tire iron and stands ready to do battle. He sizes up the trees as they near him. They are so massive that if they fight with any kind of skill, he hasn't got a chance, but he must try.

From behind the walls of elder wood, a bluebell clangs. "Round one!" bellows a trumpet vine high overhead with a good view of the proceedings.

One of the huge trees reaches out for him. Max ducks, but is smacked by another branch which swings in under his guard.

"*Oof!*" Max is taken aback. "That's an old trick. All right, you want to fight dirty, do you, you smelly old things? C'mon, c'mon," he urges them, dancing back and forth, windmilling his fists.

His right-hand opponent takes him up on the dare. It tilts a branch toward his face, following up with a sweep from a long, trailing limb which it seeks stealthily to wrap around Max from behind. Max avoids the higher branch and leaps athletically over the trailer.

"You've got to do better than that," he taunts it. He parries its next few grabs with the tire iron and then smacks it solidly on the bark when the tree leaves its guard open. The iron scores a line out of the tree, revealing the wood which begins immediately to drip sap.

Max notices that he is growing strangely tired. His strength seems to be deserting him more quickly than normal for an exercise of this type. Why, Max prides himself that he's fought shadow-boxer plants to a standstill and never broken the Marquis-of-Queens-berry rules. (Such a plant always grew near shadow-boxers and was often the only means to escape from the contentious little pugilists.) He blames the tree's magic for his fatigue but doesn't yet understand the reason.

Max sees the same tree striking out for him and notices out of the corner of his eye that the left-hand tree is doing the same thing. With no avenue open down which he can escape, Max takes the only other way out and drops to the grass. The trees' branches meet with a clash. Leaves and bits of twig fall on him. They can't reach him when he lies down. Their branches aren't long enough!

He jumps up and lays about him with the tire iron. He scores for a second time on the left-hand tree and a first on the right-hand tree, knocking a fair-sized chip out of its limb. Both trees quickly withdraw.

The left-hand tree appears to have had enough. It moves slowly away from the field, gliding without haste back into the grove. Its two comrades fill in the gap it leaves without ceasing to swing at Max. The young man curses. He had hoped to slip out between the trees, but their stately ballet is too well coordinated. On the brighter side, he has defeated one tree. He can easily beat the others.

The bluebells clang to reinforce his confidence. "Round two," bawls the trumpet flower.

"Never ask for whom the bluebell tolls," Max shouts at the two other elders. "It tolls for tree."

Without losing time, the two remaining elders pummel at Max. He is forced to drop down again and again to avoid their blows yet never has a chance to hit back. At last the right-hand tree appears to be losing momentum. Max springs up and belabors its outstretched branches with his tire iron, never noticing until it is too late that the tree is maneuvering him slowly but inexorably backward.

Suddenly aware of his danger, Max looks back over his shoulder. The other tree opens up a hinged section of its trunk like a book, revealing a hungry, lightless cubicle. Max swings harder at the tree he is facing, hoping to drive it to the end of its strength before he is forced into the other elder's box.

His struggles are in vain, for just as he strikes a blow which makes the other tree slow to a stop, he stumbles backward over something at his heels and falls into the musty cavern of the box elder. It snaps shut, blocking the sunlight out and Max in.

The inside of the box smells like old socks and moss from the underside of bridges. Max runs his hands along the inside, feeling for the split, hoping to force his way out. The very blackness unnerves him. Though damp, the heartwood is smooth, polished clean of splinters and rough places.

Lighting his lantern jaw, Max surveys his prison. It is just big enough for him to stand or sit comfortably, but not enough for him to lie down. He judges that anything up to the size of a winged deer would fit. But why do the elders capture living creatures? For that is obviously why their insides are hollow.

His light dims slightly, and he concentrates on strengthening the beam. For no reason that he can guess, he is having trouble maintaining his talent. In fact, he is growing very tired.

"There's the split," he says, his voice echoing. He puts one hand on either side of the seam, and grunting, pushes with all his strength, leaning inward to force it open. It won't budge. He falls back against the wall, panting. His hands feel very weak. He looks at them in shock. They are wrinkled and covered with crawly veins like worms. In just a few minutes, he has been aged to elderliness! So that is why Querca warned them about the trees. They suck the youth out of their prey and leave them old.

He is no longer strong enough to get out, so he is trapped inside, growing older and older until the elder chooses to let him out. At last, he feels so weak that he sits down against a wall of the elder to rest. His head nods a few times as he falls asleep, aged to gaffer's years. Max's last thoughts before he drifts off to sleep are of Onda. He is worried about her, and he's filled with regret. There's no way he can marry her now. He's far too old for her. His eyes drift closed on troubled dreams.

*Turn to section 29.*

## * **39** *

The trees circle around the three of them. Max draws his tire iron and stands ready.

"What can you possibly do with that against a tree?" Onda shrieks.

"They're elderly," Max points out. "I think they'll get tired of fighting me and go away if I hit them with this."

The three trees are closing in. Max boosts Onda up to the top of the Jack-in-the-elder-box and prepares to defend himself. "They can reach you up there, but not as easily as down here. If they try to grab you, jump off the other side!"

Onda looks down at the drop and forms a retort to fire back at Max, but he is already engaged with the elders.

Two of the elders reach out their gnarly branches for him, but he dodges away, keeping his face to them. Normally, he would prefer to have a tree at his back while fighting, but there's not a tree in this grove he can trust.

The trees surround him and wave their branches threateningly. From behind the walls of elder wood, a bluebell clangs. "Round one!" bellows a trumpet vine high overhead with a good view of the proceedings.

The third tree has flipped its shaggy gray lid, and moves ominously closer, waiting for its two cronies to grapple Max inside. It too reaches for him, its crooked limbs darting out to grab him.

Max strikes out with the tire iron, scoring a chunk of bark out of the third tree. The other two withdraw their limbs and circle again, trying to get behind him. He spins around and dances to the left, stumbling on a large root.

The trees have a smell like musty old shoes. It threatens to make Max sneeze, but he doesn't dare shut his eyes. He doesn't want a twig to escape his notice. Who knows what will happen to him if the elders succeed in boxing him up? He shoos away the sensation and twitches his nose, warning it that it had better not react.

"Hit them, Max! Get them!" Atop the Jack elder, Onda is cheering for him. He hopes that he can prevail against the trees, because they will surely go after her next.

The third tree tries again, and Max ducks under its questing branch. On his way past the bole, he whangs the tire iron into its side with a great hollow boom. The elder immediately slows down. Max sees it start its branches for him again, but it is moving as if it was underwater. The tree pauses, and then changes direction, moving away from Max, but ever so slowly.

Max almost cheers. The elders can only take so much tiring out. This boxing match will go to the challenger, and he has just won round one.

The other two don't even acknowledge their fellow's retirement. The gap has left Max with a maneuvering advantage. They can't box him in on four sides now, only three, the two of them against the Jack's tree. "C'mon, c'mon," he urges them, beckoning them forward as he jogs in place.

As soon as they go for him, Max leaps forward, ducking under branches as he did before. The great flat sides of the elders don't bend well, and since they can't extend their trailers all the way to the ground, Max has a safety zone near their roots.

He flattens himself down as much as he can and wriggles nearer his attackers.

When he drops down, the two great elders wave their branches wildly, as if accusing the other of hiding him. They begin to flap their lids at one another, squabbling in emphatic tree-talk. Meantime, Max has sneaked over and is scraping the bottom of the first box with his tire iron.

The tree lets out a tremendous clatter and shuts its lid with a bang. Max looks up in alarm, but he assures himself that it still can't reach him. He clouts it again and waits for the results.

A tremor travels up the length of the flat side, and emerges at the top as a huge, forest-rattling yawn. It too moves away from the scene of the conflict. Max has succeeded! He rolls toward his third victim before it can size up what has happened, and delivers several blows to its lower expanse. In no time at all, the field is cleared, and the bluebells ring for Max, the winner and new champion.

Onda and Brun applaud wildly, and come

down to congratulate Max. Onda descends carefully, drawing her skirt in to her knees and poking her toes into toe-holds in the rough bark. Once they are clear of the Jack's tree, Max brandishes the tire iron. "Jack! Come out now. Your boxers are all defeated." There's no answer. "Jack!" Max calls. "If you don't come out by the time I count three, I'll set your tree on fire. I'll split it into jackstraws and burn it down!"

"Oh, no you won't," the booming voice says from within the box elder.

"Oh, yes, I will," Max assures it.

"Oh, very well." The lid springs open, and twenty feet of Jack spring out of the box. "You won't hurt me now, will you?" it whimpers.

"No." Max smiles. "We want your help."

*If Max has been aged by the elders, he can restore his lost years by drinking of the Fountain of Youth.*

*Turn to section 43.*

## * **40** *

The huge face bears downward, its expression one of terror. It is hurrying to get into the hollow tree before Max can block its exit. The lid, which was originally hanging down behind the bulk of the box, is swinging up into place. Max's leap carries him to the lip just before the top of the

Jack's head vanishes inside. He brings the tire iron down.

The lid reaches the top of its arc and descends. It lands with a boom, displacing Max's tire iron, which flies through the air and lands in a small low valley, which becomes a yawning chasm where the iron strikes. Max looks alarmed at the sleepy hollow and wonders again at the power of the magician who adapted his weapon from an ordinary implement to such a formidable weapon.

"Get him," Jack pops out just long enough to scream.

From the stand of trees, three huge box elders pick up their shaggy gray roots and move in on Max. The young man has only time to retrieve his tire iron before his massive woody opponents are ringing him round. If he isn't careful, he'll be boxed in.


BOX ELDERS (3)
*To hit Max: 11   To be hit: 9   Hit points: Special
Damage: Special*


*When a box elder hits Max, he is aged twenty years. If he is hit three times, he becomes too old to fight.*


*Max uses the tire iron to fight. If he successfully hits any box elder twice, it tires out and goes away to have a nap.*

**Section 41**

*If Max wins, turn to section 33.*

*If Max loses, turn to section 42.*

* **41** *

Mere contact with the pool will probably trigger its effect, so Max avoids touching it. He leans out as far as he can and pulls the baby Onda to him by a foot. She is soaking wet and miserable. Her sob is the shrill cry of the very young infant, and it tears at Max's heart. He cradles her carefully and bundles her into the basket for warmth.

Shoving the basket into a clump of thick grass well away from the water's edge, Max begs Brun to look after it and runs to find out about the face.

He runs on tip-toe so as not to alarm the creature. There was a suspicion at the back of his mind that this was Jack. The creature's maniacal chuckling was still audible not far away. Max draws his tire iron and moves closer.

His uneasiness grows as he passes through the elder grove. He could have sworn that the box tree the size of his mother's house had been closer to the fist-shaped knoll when he first saw it. Now it was clearly several yards away. He glances over to see if perhaps there was another tree just like it, but the hummock is vacant. These trees moved!

That was what Querca had wanted them to watch out for. Well, he was on his guard now. There was no way that these boxes could box him in.

He scoots around the corner of a huge blocky tree and squats down in its shelter just as a smaller one passes by. If it was patrolling, it has missed him. Max lets out a sigh of relief. He'd better get to that noisemaker now!

He stands up and takes a deep breath, lets it out, takes another. Brandishing the tire iron, Max jumps out from his shelter and charges toward the place where he thinks the laughing face came from.

The face is where he assumed it would be, but it is even larger than he thought. Max judges that the face is as tall as he is and as wide as it is high. The neck, while not extended as far as it was, is still some twenty feet long. The painted lips are stretched wide across a chalk white face made of wood. Its wrinkled neck looks like a dull leather or cloth. And its expression, when it beholds Max, is one of sudden guilt. The crazy smile collapses and the eyes go wide. "Uh-oh!" it booms.

The neck starts to fold up into the top of an immense box elder. Max realizes that if it manages to close the lid behind it, he may never figure out what happened to Beryl Bluebird, or save Onda from her second childhood. He springs, tire iron at the ready, to keep the box from shutting.

*Roll 3 D6.*

*If the total is less than or equal to Max's value for strength, turn to section 47.*

*If the total is greater than Max's value for strength, turn to section 40.*

## * **42** *

The three trees are closing in. Max backs against the Jack-in-the-elder-box and prepares to defend himself.

Each of the trees is massive, though none is as big as the Jack tree. Max sees that fighting with them would be like hitting walls. He hefts the tire iron in his hand and hopes that it will have an effect on them. If it doesn't, and they get him, he had no idea what they'd do to him, but Onda would be next. Max had to stop them before they attacked his fiancée.

The trees surround him and wave their branches threateningly. From behind the walls of elder wood, a bluebell clangs. "Round one!" bellows a trumpet vine high overhead with a good view of the proceedings.

Max ducks to the left and dodges as one of the boxes swipes at him with an outstretched branch. He is trapped in this square ring until and unless he can send these trees away in defeat. Without axe or torch his advantages are limited. He can only hope that the tire iron is effective on all living things, not just animals and people.

He strikes out at the branch that whistles past his nose and scores a chunk of bark. The limb is swiftly withdrawn to a chorus of boos from a bamboo clump somewhere beyond the ring of trees. Max grimaces. He doesn't like bamboo. It is used to make magical fantasy fans, which when waved, make a person think he is cooler than he is. Max does not care for delusion, especially self-delusion. Obviously, he is not the favorite to win this fight. No matter; he *has* to win.

Throwing himself to his knees in front of the center tree, he drives the tire iron across the gray bark and back in a double swipe. The tree seems to pause, flapping its lid in consternation, but then a shiver travels up the trunk from where Max struck it and emerges at the top in a colossal yawn. Slowly, much more slowly than it had been moving before, the tree withdraws from the ring, leaving its two companions to catch Max.

Max stands up out of range of the tree to the right, which Max has already struck once. He notices it is moving visibly slower. It reaches for him again, but he backs up against the Jack elder. The big tree is closer than he had hoped, and the branch touches him. Max feels a sort of pull from the limb, not physical, but tangible. It is drawing something from him. He begins to feel weak and sleepy, as if he had hit himself with the tire iron. The left-hand tree, hitherto uninvolved in the fight, has opened up its box, but instead of opening upward, it opens side to side like a book. Its great gray halves part, revealing a lightless chasm. Max turns to push away from it, but forgets about the right-hand tree, and runs straight into its arms.

Though he struggles, the scratchy twigs wrap around him and force him steadily closer to the gaping trunk. He smacks the side of the open trunk with his tire iron. It slows down slightly, but it advances inexorably, swallowing him up.

Boom! Max is closed inside the box elder. It smells like old socks and moss from the underside of bridges. He runs his hands along the inside, feeling for the split, hoping to force his way out. The very blackness unnerves him. Though damp, the heartwood is smooth, without any splinters or rough places.

Lighting his lantern jaw, Max surveys his prison. It is just big enough for him to stand or sit comfortably, but not enough for him to lie down. He judges that anything up to the size of a winged deer would fit. But why do the elders capture living creatures? For that is obviously why their insides are hollow.

His light dims slightly, and he concentrates on strengthening the beam. For no reason that he can guess, he is having trouble maintaining his talent. In fact, he is growing very tired.

"There's the split," he says, his voice echoing. He puts one hand on either side of the seam, and pushes with all his strength, leaning inward to force it open. It won't budge. He falls back, panting. His hands feel very weak. He looks at them in shock. They are wrinkled and covered with crawly veins like worms. In just a few minutes, he has been aged to elderliness!

He is no longer strong enough to get out, so he continues to grow older and older. At last, he feels so weak that he sits down against a wall of the elder to rest. His head nods a few times as he falls asleep, aged to gaffer's years. Max's last thoughts before he drifts off to sleep are of Onda. He'll never be able to marry her now. He's far too old for her. His eyes drift closed.

*Go to section 29.*

## * **43** *

"And all you want me to do is to take you to where I left the Bluebird?" the Jack asks in disbelief.

"That's all," Max assures him.

"Well, you've got a deal," Jack says, his toothy grin reappearing in enamelled hues. "Let's go."

The Jack hauls his great length out of his box and inches along the ground. Max and Onda watch with fascination as he continues to pour out yard after yard, until the whole glade is filled with loops and coils of Jack-in-the-box. The rest of him is the same width as his neck, some four feet in diameter. He is quite hollow, so his flexible coils squish against each other and the trees without seeming to sustain any hurt at all.

At length, he is all the way out. His tail emerges from the box and the great lid booms shut.

Onda stifles a giggle.

"What's the matter?" Max asks. For answer, Onda points. The Jack's tail tapers down to a mere point, which is decorated with a small round brass bell. Max's mouth works. He, too, attempts to keep from laughing, but his eyes meet Onda's, and they both explode into laughter.

Jack is obviously much better at dishing it out than taking it. "What's so funny?" he demands peevishly. "Haven't you ever heard of belling the Jack? It used to be quite fashionable."

*Turn to section 37.*

## * **44** *

The Jack hauls his great length out of his box and extends along the ground, his head slightly raised up. Max and Onda watch with fascination as he continues to pour out, until the whole glade is filled with loops and coils of Jack-in-the-box. The rest of him is the same width as his neck, some four feet in diameter, but nearly ninety feet long. He is quite hollow, so his coils squish against each other and the trees without seeming to hurt him at all.

At length, he is out. His tail emerges from the box and the great lid booms shut.

Onda stifles a giggle.

"What's the matter?" Max asks. For answer, Onda points. The Jack's great length terminates in a tail which tapers down to a mere point, which is decorated with a small round brass bell. Max's mouth works. He attempts to keep from grinning too, but his eyes meet Onda's, and they both explode into laughter.

Jack is obviously much better at dishing it out than taking it. "What's so funny?" he demands, his feelings hurt. "Haven't you ever heard of belling the Jack? It used to be quite fashionable."

They apologize, but can't wipe the smiles off their faces. Affronted, the Jack slinks out of the elder grove, ignoring them. Max, Onda, and Brun follow, giggling at every jingle.

*Turn to section 37.*

## * **45** *

"What can you possibly do against three?" Onda shrieks and clutches Max's arm.

"They're elderly," Max points out. "I think they'll get tired of fighting me and go away if I hit them with this." He claps a hand to the tire iron. At least I hope so, he thinks, looking up at their great bulk.

The three trees are closing in. Max boosts Onda up on top of the Jack-in-the-elder-box and prepares to defend himself. "They can reach you up there, but not as easily as down here. If they try to grab you, jump off the other side!"

Clutching at twigs for balance, Onda measures the drop and forms a retort to fire back at Max, but he is already engaged with the elders.

Max draws his tire iron and stands ready to do battle. He sizes up the trees as they near him. They are so massive that if they fight with any kind of skill, he hasn't got a chance, but he must try. He decides that his best advantage is his agility.

Two of the elders reach out their gnarly branches for him, but he dodges away, keeping his face to them. Normally, he would prefer to have a tree at his back while fighting, but there's not a tree in this grove he can trust. Max will have to show them that he's a fierce fighter. Perhaps then he and the others will be able to get out of the grove alive. He dances from one foot to the other, judging which way the trees will sway. They don't move very quickly. He is sure he can outmaneuver them easily.

The trees surround him and wave their branches threateningly. He is ringed. Now he must fight to escape. From behind the walls of elder wood, a bluebell clangs. "Round one!" bellows a trumpet vine high overhead with a good view of the proceedings.

"C'mon, c'mon," Max urges them, shifting to the left. He hopes to get them to follow him that way, and then he'll dodge right through the gap, relying on his superior speed. One of the trees extends all its branches toward him, its twigs grasping for his flesh. Ow! That pinches!

Max ducks under the branches, avoiding their grasp. Something tells him not to let the elders touch him. They seem quite ordinary as trees go in Xanth, except for their mobility and their musty odor like that of old shoes. Small wonder there are no birds or animals in this forest. Most creatures like their homes to stay put.

As he dodges, a branch whips across his back, and Max defensively drops to the ground. That stings! Outside the ring of gray walls, a clump of bamboos boo. Max grimaces. He doesn't like bamboo. It is used to make magical fantasy fans, which when waved make a person think he is cooler than he is. Max does not care for delusion, especially self-delusion. Obviously, Max is not favored as a challenger in this event. As he rolls from one side to the other, he feels suddenly tired and slow, probably a result of the elder's slap. He was right to avoid them. They can sap his strength. He vows to be more careful.

Above his head, the tree branches swipe at him. Max discovers that they can't reach him while he is on the ground. Their branches don't extend that far. Max considers it a piece of good fortune, one he will use to win. He rolls toward the tree that hit him and belabors its roots with the tire iron. As slow moving as the tree is, it appears to hop up and down with the pain of its extremities. The ground shakes underneath it. To a chorus of boos and clanging from the bluebells, the tree retires sulkily from the ring.

Max makes a break for the gap left by the departing tree, but the two remaining immediately close ranks and box him in again. Swiftly, Max backs up against the Jack tree, dodging out of range of the other trees' limbs. The very breadth of their trunks keeps them from moving in on Max at once. They collide at the corners in their eagerness to get at him. In order to keep him from escaping, they must keep him boxed up, but it makes it harder to strike. Max discovers that this tactic gives him another advantage.

Dropping to the ground, he rolls over and over toward the left-hand tree and hits it on the root with his tire iron. Irritated, it swishes its branches impotently over his head.

"Ha ha!" he laughs. They *can't* touch him. Not only that, they can't bend over. Their broad sides are too stiff. Max clouts the tree root again, and watches in satisfaction as his second opponent throws in the towel and departs. The bluebell chorus the end of round two.

Max is left with one tree foe. This last is the

canniest of all. Max rises to his feet to dodge around it, but it matches his every move, drawing closer and closer to him until he is nearly pinned against the side of the Jack-in-the-box. It has not revealed its direct threat until now. The middle of the face nearest Max splits open like a book to reveal a deep, lightless cavity. It means to drag or push Max inside the musty-smelling box. Wildly, he swings the tire iron right and left against the branches that reach for him.

The tree moves slower and slower as the tire iron's magic takes effect, but it continues to advance inexorably toward him. In desperation, he flings the weapon into the depths of the elder box. The iron clanks against the invisible back wall, and the tree snaps shut, thinking it has Max contained. Suddenly, it begins to shiver. Max watches it warily, fearing another attack, but the bole splits open again in a huge, moldy yawn. Max holds his nose. In his opinion, the tree is long overdue for an airing. The box snaps shut, and the tree wanders away, probably looking for a nice place to take a nap. Max discovers the tire iron in the grass where it fell out of the elder's maw. He picks it up and turns against the Jack tree.

"Jack! Come out now. Your boxers are all defeated." There's no answer. "Jack!" Max calls. "If you don't come out by the time I count three, I'll set your tree on fire. I'll split it into jackstraws and burn it down!"

"Oh, no you won't," the booming voice says from within the box elder.

"Oh, yes, I will," Max assures it.

"Oh, no, you won't."

"Oh, yes, I will," Max says, more adamantly than before.

"Oh, very well." The lid springs open, and twenty feet of Jack springs out of the box. "You won't hurt me now, will you?" it whimpers, a panicked look on the painted face.

"No." Max smiles. "I want your help. First, how do I go back to being young again?" He holds out his hands. The black hair on the backs has turned gray, and the skin is wrinkling.

"There is a Fountain of Youth in the glade over that way." Jack inclines his length in the direction of the young trees. "That's all you need. Honest!"

"Ah, so that's what it was," Max nods, wonderingly. The Fountain of Youth has always been believed to be a legend. If it is the midst of this perilous forest of elders, small wonder no one has found it. He is very glad he didn't drink of it indiscriminately. That would have been a very childish thing to do. He turns to Onda. "Wait here with Brun. I'll be right back, and I'll be my youthful old self again. But if I'm not . . ." He threatens Jack with a gesture.

"You will be! You will be!" Jack is passionate in his reassurances, nodding his pointed cap.

Max dashes to the pool, avoiding the clumps of

baby elders clustered around its edge. He sees where the little boxes could easily become stumbling blocks to the unwary, and provide the Fountain with victims to youthen. He stoops at the edge of the pool and dips a small handful of water to his lips. Swiftly, Max feels his strength returning.

*Restore Max's lost years on the Character Sheet.*

"Much better," Brun whistles happily as Max approaches, looking much his young self.

"What a relief," Onda says, shaking her head. "Or a dream. Just a moment ago, I saw my whole life pass before my eyes when those big trees grabbed you."

"You saw mine, too, only from my *future*, not my past. How do I look with gray hair?" Max asks, cocking an eyebrow.

"I've *always* liked older men," Onda returns impishly.

"Now"—Max turns to the Jack—"we want you to take us to where you high-Jacked that plane tree and left Beryl Bluebird."

The Jack's eyes widen at being found out, but he nods eagerly to avoid Max carrying out any of his previous threats. "That's an easy request. Why didn't you say so in the first place?" he giggles.

*Turn to section 44.*

# * **46** *

There is no sound. Onda looks at Max and then taps again. "Jack? Please come out."

"No. You'll hurt me," Jack's voice booms, protesting.

"Come out," Max insists, pounding on the side of the box. "Or I'll burn your tree down."

"You wouldn't!"

"I sure would," Max assures him.

"You'd hurt me!"

"No," Onda puts in soothingly. "We won't hurt you if you help us."

"Oh, all right." The Jack springs up out of its box, ascending twenty feet above their heads. Max understands easily how such a tall creature could have engineered a high-jack. "What do you want me to do?"

*Turn to section 43.*

## * **47** *

The huge face bears downward, its expression one of terror. It is hurrying to get into the hollow tree before Max can block its exit. The lid, which was originally hanging down behind the bulk of the box, is swinging up into place. Max's leap carries him to the lip just before the top of the Jack's head vanishes inside. He brings the tire iron down.

The lid describes a mighty arc and slams down onto the tire iron. The Mundane metal does not give, and Max finds that he's still got the first crack out of the box. It cannot close entirely as long as the iron is there.

He pulls himself up onto the top of the box elder tree. From that vantage point, he can see the other great trees of the grove. They had all moved again, forming a semi-circle behind where he had been crouched. They were trying to box him in!

Max's resolve lends him further strength as he leans on his makeshift lever. The box top creaks a little, but doesn't budge. Undaunted, Max grasps the edge with his fingers and tries to pry it up. Still nothing. He decides to try both together, fingertips and lever. With one foot on the tire iron, he wrenches the lid up.

Complaining and groaning, the top opens about two feet. Max realizes that as soon as he lets go it is going to slam shut again. Timing his effort carefully, he hauls the lid higher and higher, grunting with the effort. Soon, it is braced against his chest, and then, on his hands which he extends up over his head. He takes a deep breath, and then he jumps into the box.

Max has a soft landing on the folds and folds of dun cloth that make up the Jack's neck. To his dismay, his tire iron has fallen with a clunk to the ground outside the box. Max feels for his second weapon, the sheathed icicle, as he commands his talent to work.

"Who are you?" the voice of the Jack booms loudly in the small enclosed space. Max's brightly gleaming lantern jaw illuminates the wide painted face. The blue eyes, each the size of Max's head, stare at him fearfully. "Why are you invading my box?"

"I'm Max. I'm here to find out what happened to Beryl Bluebird. And while I'm at it, you'd better tell me how to re-age my fiancée. She fell into the Fountain of Youth."

In spite of its worried expression, the Jack breaks into the same sort of hysterical giggles that attracted Max's attention before. "Is that all? Such an easy quest. You should have no trouble achieving your goals. But why should I tell you anything?"

"Because otherwise I'll cut all of your

clothwork," Max says evenly, brandishing the icicle. It shines with a cold glow in his chin's light.

"Oh, don't do that, no, don't do that, please!" the Jack whimpers. "I'll tell, yes, I will. Oh, my poor cloth, my poor painted head."

Max has to promise it several times that he won't hurt it before the Jack is able to speak coherently again. Through its blubbering, he understands that the Jacks, a sort of serpent, are usually quite small, but this Jack is very old, and has grown huge over many years.

"I'm the Jack-in-office here. The other trees were only protecting me. I'm their elder elder. Do you know the property of elders? No, I suppose you don't, or you wouldn't have come seeking me. All you have to do is put your baby, er, your fiancée, inside one of the boxes, and she'll grow older in no time!"

Max taps the box lid with the sickle. "Open up."

Brun perks up as he hears running footsteps coming toward him. He looks up in relief to see Max emerging from between the saplings.

"Max, Onda's sleeping like a baby now, but she kept complaining and babbling. Her body might have changed, but her mind isn't that of an infant. She's trying to tell me something."

"She must feel terribly helpless," Max says, concerned, picking up his baby betrothed. "I found the Jack. He's waiting for us over there," he indicates the direction with a thrust of his chin. "He can make Onda the right age again. And I think he knows where Beryl is."

"He does?" Joyfully, Brun flutters his wings and does a little dance in the air. A light blue tone suffuses his feathers. "Let's go!"

Under Jack's instructions, Max sets the fussing baby Onda into the box of an elder tree that is just the right size for a cradle, if she were going to remain a baby. The age magic works quickly. Max stays close to the open elder and watches as the infant grows fuzzy red hair and dainty teeth. She gets larger and larger, her arms and legs and hair lengthening. Instead of lying in the cradle, she's curled up with her knees against her chest. The baby teeth fall out and leave re-generation gaps which are filled by big adult teeth. Somehow her clothes are growing with her, which relieves Max. At this rate she has long outgrown the baby-dress her infant self had been wearing. Her figure changes from baby fat to child slender, and to adolescent beauty. "Stop," Max commands the elder as soon as Onda reaches the age she is chronologically supposed to be. "Thank you."

Onda stretches out in a wide yawn, and her hands bump into the sides of the box. Abruptly, she becomes aware of her surroundings and gazes around in fear. Her eyes meet Max's, and she calms down. "Oh! Oh, Max, what happened?"

"You fell into the Fountain of Youth. This box elder agreed to remedy your sudden youthfulness." He patted the tree which flapped its lid in pleasure.

"What must you have thought of me, doing something clumsy like that," Onda says, blushing. "Stumbling into a pond."

"You were such a beautiful baby," Max smiles as he takes her hand and gallantly helps her out of the tree.

"Thank you," she says, eyes flashing, as she stands up and smooths down her dress. Suddenly, she gets a curious look on her face, and then an expression of shock and embarrassment. "Ooh!" she exclaims. Without explanation, she rushes off into the trees.

Brun and Max watch her run away. Max looks puzzled, so the Bluebird explains. "I think her diapers were wet."

*Turn to section 43.*

## * **48** *

Onda waits and then taps again. "Jack? Please come out."

"You won't hurt me?" It sounds frightened. For such a big character, Max is not impressed with its courage.

"We wouldn't ever think of it," Onda assures it.

"Oh, all right." The Jack springs up out of its box, ascending twenty feet above their heads. Max understands easily how such a tall creature could have engineered a high-jack. "What do you want me to do?"

*Turn to section 43.*

## * **49** *

"I've got no choice," Max says grimly. "I might need it later, but I'd better use the Two Minute Replay right now, if I want to save Onda and catch that Jack."

Turning away from the kicking baby on the water's surface, Max feels around in the bushes for the fallen basket. Brun swoops over the pond. "I'll watch after her."

As quickly as he can, Max shuffles through the basket's contents, discarding a fresh, buzzing shoe-fly pie, bubble gum from a bubbling gum tree, and a pair of very large but delicate pink flowers Max recognizes with a blush as ladies' bloomers. The Hope Chest is at the very bottom.

He flings open the lid and heaves the Time Being's soap bubble gift out toward Onda. It floats gently over the water and then pops.

Max sees the sky go black for just a second, and then everything around him begins to run backwards. Brun comes flying backwards toward him, unsaying "Reh retfa hctaw ll'i."

Onda herself is inhaling giggles, and then screams as she ages back to normal. Max finds it fascinating to watch. She grows as suddenly as popcorn explodes, her arms and legs lengthening and changing, and her body altering swiftly through baby fat to mature beauty. At last, her normal self heaves upward from the water's surface, the splash settling itself back down from particles collecting in the air.

The two minutes run out suddenly, and Max has to grab Onda before she falls in again. "Eeee! Help me!" she cries, as his arms enfold her securely.

"Is that any way to treat your fiancé?" Max asks innocently, stealing a kiss. He sneaks a look back over his shoulder, and sees the Jack high over the treetops. It hasn't yet spotted him watching, so Max can get a fix on where it is in the forest. Onda hugs Max close, seeking to return the kiss. Max makes it brief, against his better judgment.

"Look up there," he whispers. "It's the Jack."

Onda's eyes go wide, but she doesn't scream. Max takes her hand and leads her into the forest as if they are unaware of the spy. Let him think they are seeking innocent pleasure.

They run through the woods on tip-toe, with Brun flying noiselessly above them. Max glances suspiciously at the elders they pass, fearing that the trees might give them away, but the elders wander aimlessly. None of them seem to notice the humans and the bird in their midst.

The Jack is in exactly the spot Max thought it would be. But as soon as they emerge from the trees, the huge painted eyes widen, and the lips lose their grin. "Uh oh!" the Jack says, and starts to descend into its box elder box.

Max races to the tree trunk and throws himself against its side, trying to keep it from shutting, but Jack, panicked, is too quick for him. The lid slams shut over the top of its head. Max slides down the flat side of the trunk and stands at the bottom picking splinters out of his hands and chin.

"Let me try," Onda says, approaching the closed box. "Jack?" She taps softly at the side. "Jack, won't you come out? We want to talk to you."

*Roll 3 D6.*

*If the total rolled is equal to or less than the value for Charisma, turn to section 48.*

*If the total is greater, turn to section 46.*

# * **50** *

Max throws himself against the box elder, reaching for the Jack. Panic-stricken, the huge spring-necked serpent collapses downward, trying to get to safety before Max can touch it.

Spotting his quarry's retreat, Max scrabbles at the side of the trunk to get up before the Jack is fully back in its box. He feels frantically for a toe-hold, but his foot finds nothing on which it can get a purchase. He slides down the bole and scrambles up again.

Even as Max is pulling himself up the tree once more, the Jack has folded itself up completely, and the lid slams down, securing it from assault. "Get him!" it cries through the box wall.

Who is it talking to? Max wonders as he gets an elbow up on the top of the tree. Perhaps, the young adventurer considers, he can pry open Jack's lid and give the big coward a talking to. They have to find out where Beryl Bluebird is being held, and Jack is the only one who knows. He must be responsible for her bird-napping. Why else would he react so guiltily when cornered?

Max has just braced the other elbow up when he feels something tapping him on the shoulder. "Max," Onda's voice cries, but it sounds much farther away than whoever is touching him. "Max, look out!" she screams.

Max turns to look over his shoulder, and surprise makes him lose his grip again. He slides all the way down the bole with his cheek scraping the rough bark and sits on the roots staring up at three enormous elders boxing him in and blocking off his escape.

**BOX ELDERS (3)**
*To hit Max: 11   To be hit: 9   Hit points: Special*
*Damage: Special*

*When a box elder hits Max, he is aged twenty years. If he is hit three times, he becomes too old to fight.*

*Max uses the tire iron to fight. If he successfully hits any box elder twice, it tires out and goes away to have a nap.*

*If Max wins, turn to section 45.*

*If Max loses, turn to section 38.*

*If Max has the Two Minute Replay and chooses to use it, turn to section 36.*

# * **51** *

"What, you scratched by a little salad like that?" Fortinbrass laughs. "Well, you fight well enough to be a brassy, but that soft hide of yours needs some reinforcing. Fortunately, there's a healing spring that bubbles up through the green stuff not far from here. Sit tight, and I'll bring you to it."

Onda pats Max's forehead with her dainty handkerchoo, and the little cloth fingers tenderly stroke his brow. The catamaran glides over the sticky marsh with as little trouble as though it was sailing through clear water. The way to the healing spring is not a direct one. Fortinbrass steers around enormously bloated jelly-barrel trees that seem to flourish with their roots in the green cream, making trifling little islands here and there.

"Whoa," commands the brassy, pointing out a fountainlet to the humans. "There she blows. Try a sip. It'll put you right."

Max dips his hands into the clear liquid and draws a cupped handful to his mouth. The spring looks like a hole dug down through the murky water, and the water bubbles around his hands like soda poppy pop. He feels better even before he tastes the potion.

"Here, Brun," Max offers the Bluebird a fresh

sip. The little bird hops feebly to his wrist and takes a drink of healing potion. Some color comes back to the Bluebird's feathers, and Max begins to think that they will be able to save his little friend from dying of unhappiness.

*Return all Max's hit points to the character sheet.*

*Turn to section 60.*

## * **52** *

"What, you scratched by a little salad like that?" Fortinbrass laughs. "Well, you fight well enough to be a brassy, but that soft hide of yours needs some reinforcing."

Fortinbrass sorts through a box under his seat and emerges with a little brass chest. "My mother made me take these with me. She never stops worrying, even though I keep telling her I'm grown up." Putting to one side a sweater knitted of steel wool, he removes from the box several small brass scales and applies them to Max's wounds. "These are skinflints. They'll heal where it hurts and protect the places until you're healed like you were made of solid stone. When you're all fixed up, they'll fall off."

"Thank you," Max says, ringing one of the skinflints with the tip of his finger. It lets out brassy tone, but the wound underneath doesn' hurt. The brassies' medicine was very effective!

"Have a drink," Fortinbrass offers, dipping marshmallow into a brass cup and handing it around. "There's reputed to be a healing spring hereabout, though I've not found it yet. Cheers." Max downs the cupful.

"Here, Brun," Max offers the Bluebird a fresh sip. The little bird hops feebly to his wrist and takes a drink of healing potion–laced marshmallow. Some color comes back to the Bluebird's feathers, and Max begins to think that they will be able to save his little friend before he dies of unhappiness.

*Roll 1 D6, add to Max's hit points.*

*Turn to section 60.*

## * **53** *

"Yes, thanks. Oh, wait, there's still something in the Hope Chest." Max looks greedily at the cereals, considering their potential. Those certainly must have stronger magic than two minutes time replayed would. "I'd hate to see it go to waste. Would you like a spell, Colonel? It reverses time for two minutes. I suppose one can use it to correct a mistake one makes, if it was made less than two minutes before."

"Yes, indeed, happy to take it off your hands.

Good strategic use, that two minutes, what? A war can be won or lost by magic or extreme cleverness, but there's nothing like good old-fashioned hindsight to change bad planning to bad luck." The old fellow chuckles. "Ha, functional hindsight. Thank you. Thank you indeed."

Max runs for the Hope Chest and fills it up with the minuscule seeds. "Best to get it now while it's tiny," the colonel encourages him. "You can fit more into the container that way."

*Turn to section 55.*

## * **54** *

Max looks greedily at the seeds, but remembers that the Two Minute Replay is still in Onda's Hope Chest. He weighs the benefits of each, and decides that the Time Being's gift is a more powerful and more versatile magic than the Daytime Cereal. With regret, he shakes his head.

"Sorry, sir. I've just remembered, the Hope Chest has something in it I'd rather not lose. Thank you anyway."

"Hope you don't regret the missed opportunity, my boy, but it's your choice." The colonel leads him back to the party.

*Turn to section 55.*

## * **55** *

In the morning, Max and the others join the bogeys for a hearty breakfast consisting of mush from mushrooms and pink grapes plucked from a pink grapefruit tree. Onda returns the petti-coat to the colonel's lady. Max peers at the garment curiously, since he wasn't allowed to see it at the party.

"Sure you won't keep it, love?" the bogey woman asks kindly, looking at Onda's ragged dress and waistcoat.

"Thank you, no. It's a little tight," Onda confesses.

They say their farewells and leave the bogey encampment, guided by Peat, who waves a sad good-bye from the edge of the bogey territory as Max, Onda, and Brun head south.

*Turn to section 66.*

## * **56** *

"Your story has touched me," the colonel says, blowing through his moustache and wiping his round eyes with a handkerchoo he takes from his sleeve. "I apologize for any inconvenience you may have suffered. Summon the bird. He shouldn't be wandering around out there. Bird-eating chobees have been spotted as recently as last night. You are invited to remain here through mess and overnight too, if you desire."

"Mess?" Onda asks fastidiously. A bogey appears behind her with a chair and assists her to sit down in it.

"Mealtime, miss. Begins soon as the cook hops to it." Max looks around him for a one-legged bogey crossing the campground, but decides that it is just a figure of speech.

The colonel waves Max to a seat, too. "Meantime, talk to an old soldier. It isn't often I have such agreeable company." The colonel leans forward amiably and pats Onda's hand in a fatherly fashion. "Would you like some sherry? It isn't imported, alas, I cannot tell a lie. We press it from the fruit of our own sherry trees. We do a great deal for ourselves here."

His boast isn't surprising to the two young humans. The little orange humanoids are very efficient. They run to prepare dinner. Some, with cauldrons of water and warming pans of hot peppers, thread their way to where the vegetable patch is sewn beside a needle pine. One contingent of orange bogeys carries armfuls of beef-steak tomatoes to a roasting pit. Soon the air is full of the mouth-watering aroma of cooked meat. A rating appears before the colonel and snaps out a bone-cracking salute. "Orange Company reports dinner is ready, SAH!"

The chief stands up and holds out a hand to Onda. "Young lady, if I may escort you?" Onda is nearly a foot and a half taller than her guide, but he makes up for it in grandeur.

Max follows along behind and is politely seated at table to the colonel's left. Bogeys are similar in size to goblins, but they couldn't be more different in temperament. Where goblins are rude and crass, the bogeys are fastidiously polite. "We're a long-distance outpost of the empire, you might say," the colonel comments to Onda. "Standards to maintain. Truth to tell, though, we've not heard from our command post in about a hundred years."

"Oh, that's terrible," Onda sympathizes.

"It's not so bad, miss," the colonel assures her. "No surprise inspections, you know."

The meal is excellent. Max has no idea why they call it a mess, unless the bogeys are referring to what is left after the meal is over.

"You are fortunate to have come today," their host tells them, as dessert is served. "Tonight is our cotillion. It will be a great party. Um," he surveys Max's ragged costume. "Don't suppose you brought a coat?"

"No. Sorry."

"Never mind. We have enough and to share. I'll summon my coterie."

In no time, Max is fitted with a very stylish coat, elaborately decorated with jewels and feathers. It is a bit short in the arms and wide in the body, but it is long enough to be comfortable.

## Section 56

Every one of the bogeys is wearing a marvelously fancy coat. Max has never attended a cotillion before, but it seems to have a lot to do with the heavy outer garments. Even the bogey ladies were be-coated.

The colonel's lady tries in vain to fit Onda into something from her own wardrobe, but the girl can wear none of her hostess's somewhat large garments except one, a very small petti-coat. Onda tries it on discreetly inside the tent and pronounces it to be a perfect fit. She refuses to display it to Max or any of the others. "I'm wearing it under my clothes. That's enough," she declares, as they take their places for the dance.

The entertainment begins with a display of precision marching and whistling by the colonel's own squadron. Max applauds with the others in admiration of their skill. Next, the colonel himself gets up to do a patter song, in which the punchline to every verse is, "I am the very model of a modern bogey colonel," pronouncing every syllable to make the rhyme come out right. The others all seem to know the words and enjoy reciting them along with their commanding officer. Then the dancing begins. The types of music bogeys enjoy range from the very long hair music sung by a group of yaks to rock music rendered by a mockingbird who used its magic to assume the illusory form of the gigantic red bird.

Onda's skill as a dancer attracts the eye o every male at the party. She dances the firs dance with Max and the second with the colonel, who surrenders his lady to the tall human male. After that, she is whirled around the clearing by every bogey who can scrape an introduction, leaving Max to make shift for himself. "Hey, don't be a bog hog," one soldier accuses another and bows to Onda. "May I have the pleasure of this dance?"

Max finds that these strange orange people can really bogey down when they want to. He enjoys himself tremendously, but his feet protest his adding an evening of dancing on top of a long day's hike. Excusing himself from a tittering orange maiden, he wanders away to look at the moon.

Forewarned against the region's dangers, he is careful to stay within the camp's confines. The soldiers unlucky enough to be pulling guard duty tonight explain to him that it is dangerous to go beyond the markers on the ground and trees at the camp's perimeter. Max stays within the line of moonstones, which reflect the almost fullness of the moon shining in the sky.

The moon is peeking out between two big fluffy clouds wearing their nighttime gray. He wonders why they don't stay white all the time but camouflage themselves in the night sky. Probably it is because clouds are notoriously practical jokers and like to sneak up and surprise benighted travelers with rainstorms they can't tell are coming. He stares into the southern sky, wondering how much farther it is to the Phantom Ranch, whatever that is, and hoping that Beryl Bluebird is still alive and well. Brun is growing weaker daily. Max is deeply concerned, but there's nothing further he can do to help until the morning.

Just as Max is turning away, something white in the moonlight catches his eye. He swivels back and jumps in shock. A ghost erupts right out of the underbrush, waving its arms in his face. He emits a yell of surprise and fear, until he remembers that ghosts can't hurt him, but they certainly are effective at scaring people. This one has its sheet waving wildly, exposing a bony skeleton and hollow-socketed eyes.

"Doooon't gooooo!" it shrieks. "Leeeeave the Ghoooost Wriii-ter aloooooone!"

Max gawks at the apparition and swallows hard. Sometimes it is difficult to remember that ghosts are immaterial. This one can't hurt him. Ghosts are only the spirits of beings that die of murder or suicide. Max tries to convince himself that it's only a coincidence that it is warning him against the Ghost Writer. How could it know anything about him when its bones must be buried close to the bogey camp? Unless the Writer killed the man or woman to whom this restless spirit belongs. Is the mysterious Writer a killer, as well as a kidnapper?

"Dooooon't goooo!" it groans again and then dissolves into the moonlight. Max is shaken, but he is still resolved to pursue Beryl Bluebird' captor.

He scents something sweet growing a little to his right. Carefully treading inside the line of glowing stones, Max finds himself staring at the camp cereal patch. The standing grain smells fresh and good. He wonders if there might be some mature roats in the lot. Those would make him a tasty breakfast. He reaches out to break off some ripe heads and rubs the kernels between his palms.

"Yo-ho, human," comes a hearty voice from behind him.

"Good evening, Colonel," Max greets him politely.

"Yes, hmm. Came out to see the moonlight. Always good this time of night. Oh, I say, don't taste those!" Colonel Bogey whips his ever-present goff club around and knocks the seeds out of his hand. Max looks at him in shock. "Sorry old boy, but these are no ordinary cereals. Mustn't be tasted."

Max looks at the moonlimned sheaves waving softly in the night breeze. "Why not? They don't look like wild oats or anything dangerous like that."

"They're far more dangerous. These are Daytime Cereals," the colonel announces, rolling back on his heels in the style of any lecturer. "Found them in a vast wasteland far away from here. They grow amazingly fast, which is why we tried them out for rations, but they were a disappointment. Mostly insipid, occasionally tasteless. Very popular among goblins and Mundanes, you know. But there's no more nourishment in them than there is in the husk of any other grain."

"That figures." Max smirks. Mundanes would eat anything. "Aren't they good for anything at all?"

"Mundanes? Oh, yes, you mean the cereal. Ha ha! Well, we use them for the odd surprise capture. They spring up so fast that we can plant them in the path as the creature we want to catch is walking toward us. When it stops at the patch for a taste, we know that we have it. Any creature that tries 'em 'll eat them day in and day out. Attractive smell, you may have noticed. Daytime Cereals are positively addictive."

"Well, if they're daytime cereals, can't your quarry escape at night?"

"No, not really. It's at night that these little grains become dangerous." The bogey pokes the standing cereal with his club. It doesn't even notice. "But that's when we pick 'em for strategic use. They shrink down so countless grains can fit into a pocket. My sappers gather them. Dangerous work, since at daybreak they explode back to their original size unless they're packed away. Nighttime Mini-Cereals are more addictive than their daytime version. Most popular. And since there are so many nocturnal animals in Xanth, we can capture more creatures at night than in the day. But the grain has to be carried in something that holds them inert or they'll sprout."

"What could one use to take some?" Max inquires. "Not that I'm asking for any," he finishes hurriedly.

"I don't see why you shouldn't have some if you want them. We're all immune to them here, ha ha! Closed containers, preferably magical ones, is what you use. Once we clear the nuts out of a chestnut chest, we employ those for maneuvers."

"My wife has a Hope Chest from a cedar chestnut," Max suggests.

"That would do nicely. Hope is one of those difficult intangibles. Anything that can contain that may transport this grain without incident. How about it, laddie?"

*If Max wants to take some Daytime Cereals, and he still has the Two Minute Replay, turn to section 53.*

*If Max wants to take some Daytime Cereals, and the Hope Chest is empty, turn to section 58.*

*If Max doesn't want any Daytime Cereals because he still has the Two Minute Replay, turn to section 54.*

*If he doesn't want any for any reason, turn to section 59.*

# * **57** *

Max is filled with dread as two monsters rise out of the mire on his side of the boat. They appear to be nothing more than masses of sharp-edged ribbon weeds, but they move with deliberate malice. Max has trouble identifying the head until a dark green orifice opens just above the center of the mass of weeds, showing long dark brown thorns arranged as a beast's teeth would be. Steadying himself, Max rises to his feet. To his surprise, Cat O'Moran rides calmly and rocks very little even though two heavy men are standing up in her. She does list toward the solid metal brassie, who is probably double Max's weight. Onda is holding on firmly amidships, trying to avoid messy droplets of marsh that spatter around her. Max draws the icicle, sweeping its silvery crescent back and forth to test the balance. The samphires roar.

Fortinbrass has already engaged one of the samphires that surges up on the other side of the boat. The brassy has his hands wound tightly in the trailing marshweed and is throttling any streamers that come within his reach. Max glances back to keep his mind on what *he* is doing and trusts that the brassy can maintain things over there.

Hissing, a samphire reaches for Max. Its long weedy limbs wrap wetly around him. Max's ribs creak as the marsh monster tightens its coils. It intends to suffocate him and drag him with it into the mire to drink his blood at its leisure. "Never!" he shouts heroically. The young man cuts furiously at the monster with the icicle, noting with satisfaction as it slices cleanly through the leaves and stems, scattering them in the air. Severed pieces of samphire wriggle for a fresh grip, spurting ichor all over the boat and its inhabitants.

Max fights grimly on. His bare legs are becoming tied up in creepers as the samphire winds around them, trying to trip him up. Even vines and hanging moss from the surrounding trees get into the act, draping themselves over Max's eyes so he can't see his opponent. The wounded weed's companion joins it and throws sticky tendrils around the young man's body. Onda screams as her fiancé disappears in the mass of green trailers. Gradually, the white icicle appears, chopping away bits of greenery.

With a tremendous wrench, Max pulls his other hand free. Putting the sickle between his teeth, he hastily wraps some limp severed bands of samphire leaf, which are three inches wide and many yards long, around and around his hand. As soon as the samphire realizes Max's arms are free, it seeks to recapture them, hissing fearsomely through its vegetable teeth. Max slashes with the sickle, severing another mass of weed, and punches powerfully into the gaping mouth with his wrapped hand.

Triumphant, the samphire closes its jaws on what it thinks is tasty human flesh. Max withdraws his hand from the thick wadding as the thorns mesh. The samphire soon discovers it is chewing on a section of itself and roars furiously. Blindly, it reaches for anything it can grapple, and pulls tree limbs, vines, even a section of Max's tunic toward its hungry maw. Now that it is no longer fighting with any strategy, Max can chop it to bits without trouble.

To his dismay, the healthy samphire, which was intertwined with and indistinguishable from the wounded plant, begins to send out creepers that latch on to his arms and legs. Max realizes it has tricked him and struggles valiantly to disentangle himself. It has a firm grip on his left leg, which it is drawing out from under him, upsetting his balance. He slashes at the vines pulling at him. The toothy orifice evades the sickle sweeps and moves in closer. Max chops again.

The vines yank hard and the thorns close on his thigh. Agony shoots through his muscles so that he nearly drops the sickle in the marsh. He recovers himself in time to chop away at the controlling knot of weeds until his blows begin to land dangerously close to his own leg. He feels his leg weaken. There must be some venom in the samphire's thorns that cause its victims to go limp for easier eating. He does not give up and manages to hew away the remaining mobile fronds. With one final heave, he pulls loose the vines around his leg and tosses them far out over the surface of the marsh where they sink messily into the glop. Panting, he plops down onto the catamaran's bench. Fortinbrass is already sitting there next to Onda who leans forward to hug Max tightly.

"That was so brave," she whispers to him, her eyes shining.

Max shakes his head. "What horrible monsters!"

"What took you so long, my boy?" the brassy interrupts them, showing his gleaming teeth. "I finished with mine long ago."

"I'll trade you hides the next time," Max says, wiping his hair out of his eyes and kissing Onda.

*If Max does not need any healing, turn to section 60.*

*If Max has sustained any wounds, Roll 3 D6.*

*If the total rolled is less than or equal to Max's value for Luck, turn to section 51.*

*If greater, turn to section 52.*

## * 58 *

"Yes, thanks." Max looks greedily at the cereals, considering their potential. He runs for the Hope Chest and fills it up with the minuscule seeds.

"Best to get it now while it's tiny," the colonel encourages him. "You can fit more into the container that way. Only sensible, good strategic planning to be prepared. Don't forget, keep them shut up in the chest or suffer the consequences. You don't have years to become acclimated to their effect."

"I'll be careful," Max promises.

*Turn to section 55.*

## * 59 *

Max looks greedily at the seeds, but wonders if he wouldn't be putting himself in more danger by taking this magical cereal than by leaving it behind. With regret, he shakes his head.

"Sorry, sir. I've just decided I don't want to risk my life with magic I don't understand. I'm content to go on defending myself and my wife in more ordinary ways."

"Hope you don't regret the missed opportunity, my boy, but it's your choice." The colonel leads him back to the party.

*Turn to section 55.*

*Turn to section 55.*

## \* **60** \*

Wiping away gobs of the sticky marshmallow, Max helps Fortinbrass tie up Cat O'Moran at the far side of the sweet swamp.

"Good luck to you," the brassy insists, shaking hands all 'round. "Knock 'em dead. The ones that aren't yet, of course."

"Good luck with your romance," Onda wishes him. "I'm sure your parents will come to understand how you feel."

"Oh, not those copper-bottoms. But after seeing how happy the two of you are, I'm definitely in favor of matrimonial bliss." Fortinbrass's smile was bright. "Farewell, you three. Come on, Cat, let's go!"

The travelers wave good-bye and set off on the path leading south.

It is a hot noon. Brun is too tired to perch on either humans' shoulders and is asleep in a nest made from a small blanket leaf in the depths of Onda's basket. Stopping frequently for cool drinks and rests makes Max feel more frustrated for allowing himself to be tricked by the Jack. "I feel like such a fool," he tells Onda. "It cost us another day. Poor Brun won't last much longer."

"He'll hold on," Onda promises him. "There's nothing stronger than love." She squeezes Max and slips her hand into his arm.

"Wait," Max says, stopping in his tracks and listening. He thrusts back a hand to halt Onda. "Something's—a lot of somethings are coming this way." He can hear many beings whistling a tune and walking in cadence along the curving path. If he and Onda keep moving, they would meet—whoever it was. Max is ill prepared to defend his lady love and Brun from numbers of hostile monsters. He wishes again that she had stayed at home in the South Village.

Onda draws back against a jelly-barrel tree, cradling the basket protectively to her breast. The Bluebird's head pokes out between her hands and cranes an ear toward the noise, a puzzled expression on his little face.

"What's going on?" he asks sleepily.

"Who is it?" Onda breathes nervously.

Max peers over the tops of the thickly clustered clumps of grass. All that is visible of the approaching threat is a slim metal pole with a scored oval of metal attached sideways to its end.

"Whoever it is, they hate goffs," Max comments. "That's a goff club."

The whistling gets louder. Max tests the branches of the spreading jelly tree, but they are soft and flabby, unsuitable to climb or for use as weapons. He looks at his hands, and admits that they are in a sticky situation. All the other trees in the vicinity are too narrow to hide behind. They'll have to take their chances on secreting themselves in the undergrowth.

"I just hope it doesn't decide to grass on us," Brun complains, not liking the thinness of the ground cover. He always preferred a nice high nest. "Jump for it, here they come!"

Together, Max and Onda plunge into the nose-high grass, closing the sheaves behind them to hide their passage.

They are only just in time. As Max peers anxiously out at the pathway, a single file of beings troops past them. These creatures are pudgy bipeds about four feet high, which explains why Max hadn't seen them clearly. Their skin is a dull orange, and their round cheeks puff out as they whistle their way along in perfect step with one another. At the head of the file is a larger being, the same color, but wearing a curious helmet, like an inverted bowl with a wide brim. He is the one waving the goff club.

"Bogeys!" Max exclaims, remembering just in time to keep his voice down. "I sure am glad they didn't see us."

He is abruptly elbowed in the ribs. Astonished, he turns to see Onda holding her nose pinched closed. "It's not grass! It's peppermint!" she whispers urgently.

Too late, Max feels the tickling begin in his

own sinuses. "I just noticed," Max apologizes, tears of irritation pouring out of his eyes. "I—can't—*Wha-CHOO!*"

"Colonel!" One of the bogeys stops right in front of their hiding place and parts the grasses, revealing Max, Onda and Brun, all sneezing pitifully.

"Uh-oh," Max snuffles. "Bogey at twelve o'clock high."

The colonel bogey marches down the line to confront them. "Spies," he booms, waving the club under their reddening noses (and beak), and clapping it into place under one meaty arm. "Spies! Seize them!"

Several of the bogeys hop to, obeying their chief's order. They bind Max and Onda fast with strands of quickgrass. Max's heart sinks. He has no hope of being able to wiggle loose from these bonds. Others attempt to capture Brun by sprinkling salt on his tail, but the little Bluebird avoids the heavy grains and leaps into flight. He follows the two humans and their captors and flutters high above their heads all the way to the bog.

"That way," the colonel directs, pointing his goff club toward a break in the marsh grasses. Onda looks through, wrinkling her nose distastefully.

"It's all muddy in there," she protests. "I'll ruin my shoes."

"Prisoners will obey orders!" the bogey man shrieks, his face contorting horribly. He reminds Onda of a nightmare or two she once had, and she backs away. The bogeys of the rank force Onda and Max to march into the bog. The guards' brusque attitude doesn't extend to physical contact. They lead the humans carefully. Max watches his guard's feet to ensure he won't make a misstep. One false move, and he could be up to his neck in green goo. With his hands bound, he is unable to stop himself from falling or even to brush away the leaves hitting him in the face. Much shorter than he, the bogeys aren't troubled by the trailing creepers. One lands on Max's head, creeps down into his shirt, out a tear across his back, and begins an examination of his right boot until a bogey slaps it away.

"Get a move on, get a move on," the orange creature orders him. "Don't go getting bogged down. That's *our* job." He roars with laughter, and his comrades join in. "A joke, sir."

"Oh, yes," Max nods, determined to be agreeable. "Ha ha ha!"

"Silence in the ranks!" roars the colonel.

Onda picks her way as daintily as she can, but her feet and legs are becoming spattered and streaked with mud. She is afraid of snakes and other creepy-crawlers that exist in the marshes and fens up north. If she is unlucky, one of them will mistake her legs for narrow trees, and she might be bitten . . . somewhere. She pulls her sensible skirt closer about her legs and hopes the hem won't get too filthy.

The bogeys don't seem to pay any attention to her. "Not plump enough to be pretty." "Or short enough. Much too tall," they say to each other, just loud enough to be audible to the girl. Onda is just a trifle hurt that they don't find her attractive, but relieved.

The rank-and-file bogeys don't mind the muck and mire. Their whistling doesn't falter once while they tramp along the narrow path. "It's where we come from," Max's escort explains. "Bogs generate bogeys. All the best people come from bogs."

"I come from a village," Max offers. "I'm called Max."

"Poor thing," observes the bogey. "M'name's Peat. Oo's the bird up there? Oi've noticed 'im follering us back along."

Max never has a chance to answer, for at that moment they reach the bogey encampment. Silently, he wills Brun to stay out of sight. To a stimulating fanfare of bogshorns, they are marched into a clearing surrounded by camouflage tents in bright speckled pink, streaked brown, smudged green and translucent orange to blend in with the jungle flowers, the creepers, the mud, and the bogeys. Another sort of rhubarb awaits them, as the off-duty bogeys speculate noisily among themselves who the prisoners are, and where they come from.

Max can see it is a crack military organization. A muscat-tree grows oily-smelling muskets in great profusion. Max knows that they aren't very powerful weapons; all they fire is grapeshot. Several lines of infant-trees line one side of the camp, with all the tough babies growing on them clad in battle gear. To the crossbeam of a henge made of wood are nailed several goff heads. The colonel appears to be serious about his game. Most of them are unmarked, but there is a hole in one. Cherry bomb trees grow in a tight cluster immediately before the largest pavilion to which the colonel strides. Two very short bogeys hurry inside and come out bearing a plain camp chair. They set it down at the tent door just under the shade of the flap held up by two wooden standards. The colonel dusts the seat off with a flick of his club and plants his round behind in the chair.

"Bring the prisoners forward," he bellows.

Peat bows low and ushers the two humans before his chief. Onda is frightened and presses close to Max. The young man smiles encouragingly at her and then faces the choleric orange Colonel Bogey.

"Now, spies, who are you?" the bogey demands. "And what are you doing in our patrol territory?"

"We're not spies. We had no idea that this territory was being patrolled by you or anyone else," Max begins. "We were just crossing. . . ."

"Just crossing? By the marsh that spawned us, what do you think patrols are supposed to prevent? Unauthorized crossing!" The colonel must have authorized himself, for he is very cross indeed.

"Please, let me explain," Max asks, putting on

as charming a smile as he can muster. The colonel nods, and Max unfolds his story. ". . . And we must cross through your, er, patrol territory to reach the Phantom Ranch to rescue Beryl Bluebird. We're sorry to be trespassing, but we're strangers around here."

"Hmm," hmms the colonel, weighing their story and smacking the club into his plump hand.

*Roll 3 D6.*

*If the total is less than or equal to Max's value for Charisma, turn to section 56.*

*If the total is greater, turn to section 62.*

## * **61** *

Max is filled with dread as two monsters rise out of the mire on Max's side of the boat. They appear to be nothing more than masses of sharp-edged ribbon weeds, but they move with deliberate malice. Max has trouble identifying the head until a dark green orifice opens just above the center of the knot of weeds, showing long dark brown thorns arranged as a beast's teeth would be. Steadying himself, Max rises to his feet. To his surprise, Cat O'Moran rides calmly and rocks very little even though two heavy men are standing up in her, one double the weight of the other. Onda is holding on firmly amidships, trying to avoid droplets of marsh that spatter around her. Max draws the icicle, sweeping its silvery crescent back and forth to test the balance.

Fortinbrass has already engaged one of the samphires that surges toward him. The brassy has his hands wound tightly in the trailing marshweed and is throttling any streamers that come within his reach. Max glances back to keep his mind on what *he* is doing and trusts that the brassy can maintain things on that side.

Hissing, a samphire reaches for Max. Its long weedy limbs wrap around him tightly, squeezing his ribs in its coils. It means to suffocate him and drag him with it into the mire to drink his blood at its leisure. Max has no intention of letting a vegetable eat him. He must kill it before it breaks all of his bones.

With a yell, Max slices across the ribbons, severing many and scattering leaves and stems in the air. The cut lengths of samphire sway wildly, spraying ichor all over the young man. Sputtering, Max splashes again and dashes the sap from his face with his sleeve. His foe lets out a vegetable roar that parallels any dande-lion that Max has ever heard. It goes berserk, slapping its tentacular tendrils around anything it can reach and pulls tree limbs, vines, even a flap of Max's torn tunic toward its gaping maw.

One of the wildly swinging vines smacks the

young man in the side of the head. Ear ringing, Max redoubles his offensive, swinging the sickle through the thickest parts of the samphire's body. With the monster spreading its attack so thin, it is no challenge for him to chop the wounded samphire to bits. Soon, he'll have defeated his half of the menace. He wonders how Fortinbrass is doing.

Suddenly, whole creepers of full strength begin to insinuate themselves around Max's extremities. Max looks down in amazement at the vines around his ankles and can't connect them with the nearly dead samphire at his feet. It can't possibly be attacking with such fervor. There must be a second marshweed!

Max flails around him with the icicle, but he is clearly at a disadvantage. He can't locate the nerve center of his new adversary, and it is getting the better of him. What is showing above marshmallow level must be only the half of the creature. Its limbs are thicker and longer than the small samphire he has already defeated. Onda screams.

"Max! Up there!"

The young man continues to fight, but he risks a glance above him and immediately wishes he hadn't. The other half of the giant samphire has emerged from the depths, dripping goo, and its thorny mouth is at least twice the diameter of the first weed's.

Wrenching his sickle arm free of the questing

tendrils, Max swings the weapon in an arc upward, but his shoulder is caught by a length of samphire. The mouth moves downward, thorn-teeth dripping marshmallow and digestive fluid. This one isn't waiting to drag him under the surface to feed.

Struggling furiously, Max seeks to evade the samphire's fangs. He manages to hook into the nerve center with the end of the sickle blade, but his thrust is without power. The weed has been steadily squeezing his lungs flat, and he is too out of breath and in too much pain to fight well.

The samphire lowers its maw and clamps it right through the fabric of his tunic into his shoulder and neck. Slurping greedily, it feasts on his blood. Max's struggles grow weaker and weaker, until Onda's screams are a whistling echo in his ears. What he can see through the draping creepers is growing dark.

"Hold on, sport," Fortinbrass shouts, leaping over from his side of the boat to Max's aid. Pieces of strangled samphire decorate the catamaran's narrow sides, and the remains of the bodies bubble as they sink slowly into the depths. "Give over, you hypertrophied vegetable," the brassy taunts the samphire. It snarls and slaps him away. He reaches into the heart of the green knot with both hands and squeezes tightly anything he encounters. The samphire lets out a pained squeal and unloops a few of its streamers to attack the brassy.

## Section 61

Fortinbrass just stands smiling as the weed wraps itself around him and continues to strangle and tear. Onda watches him in fear, and he winks boldly at her just before the frustrated samphire covers his face.

"Don't you worry, Onda," he calls, his voice somewhat muffled by the leaves. "This soft salad can't hurt me." In a short time, the samphire gives way to internal distress, and lets go of Fortinbrass. Slowly, agonizingly, he peels the vines away from Max, who collapses to the deck of Cat O'Moran.

"Hey, friend, are you all right?" Fortinbrass examines Max's neck, which has several deep wounds oozing blood and sap.

Onda listens to his chest. Max's heart is beating, but his breathing is ragged and painful. "Thank goodness. He's alive," the girl announces, biting her lip.

"Can I do anything?" Fortinbrass asks, concerned.

"Just get me to dry land," Onda says, pulling out the little box containing the fast overland snail. "I have to send a message for help. He's too ill to finish the quest, and I'm desperately afraid that Brun may die."

Silently for once, the brassy commands his feline craft to the edge of the marsh, and Onda releases her little messenger.

*Turn to section 29.*

# * **62** *

"A greater load of codswallop I've never heard, and I've known many a contentious cod, let me tell you," the colonel says, his face turning the color of a sunset. "Lock them up. No," he says, holding a pudgy orange finger in the air. "Tonight is the cotillion. The ladies must not be troubled by the sight of intransigent itinerants. Throw them out!"

"This way, miss," Peat Bogey says, leading them away from the choleric colonel. Once out of the encampment, the soldier pulls them to one side of the gate.

"There's another path yer might want to try, heads the way you're going. Only yer'll have to skirt the camp pretty closely, or the carnivorous plants'll get yer. Got it?" The bogey winks conspiratorily at them. "Stay outside the moon-stone barrier, and yer'll know where yer are. Best o' luck t'two of you."

Max seizes the creature's hand and pumps it. "Thanks for your help."

"Oo, nothin'. Too bad yer not stayin' for the party. It'll be a bang. G'bye." Pulling at his forelock, Peat scampers back into the clearing.

Max glances right and left to make sure no sentries are observing them, and leads Onda around to the south side of the bogeys' camp. "We have to find a place to stay tonight pretty soon. It's getting late."

"I know. I'm hungry. Where's Brun?"

"Here." The Bluebird flies down to them from a nearby hollywooden vine where he had been nearly invisible among the vine's bright lights. He perches on Max's shoulder and hangs on as the young man pushes his way through the heavy vegetation surrounding the bogeys' camp.

The trees are thick with movie trailers, a particularly long-lived creeper heavy with cellulose. Some of the vines are quite pretty, each inch showing a slightly different colored picture than the inch before. Some are faded duds. Others are quite horrible, especially the talkies that roar and chatter as the humans brush against them. Popcorn plants and caramel apple trees wave their fruit high above their heads.

"Mmm! What's that delicious smell?" Max's nose tips upward to catch an elusive scent in the hot air. He surges ahead, holding the branches out so they won't slap at Onda. Without paying attention to the line of moonstones he steps over, Max walks into a patch of grain growing at the southwest edge of the bogeys' land. It smells toasty and sweet and very edible.

"What is it?" Onda asks, looking at the ripe heads of grain.

"I don't know, but doesn't it smell good?" Brun asks, eyeing it hungrily.

Max thinks hard, trying to identify the grain. It isn't roats, one of his favorite foods. It isn't rye; there is no telltale scent of alcohol. But it smells delicious, and he's tired and hungry. He plucks a few stalks.

*If he chooses to eat some of it, turn to section 65.*

*If he chooses to go hungry, turn to section 78.*

## ✳ **63** ✳

"In fact, it tastes sort of boring," Max adds, looking at the remaining kernels. He makes a face. "It's insipid. Don't eat any. I think there's something strange about it, too, something magical."

He throws away the remainder and has to jump back when the grains sprout almost instantly. "Great Xanth!" he exclaims. "What a potential defensive weapon. You can grow grain instantly and distract something that's chasing you with that delicious aroma. Too bad we can't eat them. I'm going to take a sample of it with us. Maybe when we get home Clem Centaur can tell me what it is."

Max picks more and puts them into his tunic pocket, trying not to be dismayed at the disappointed expressions on Onda's and Brun's faces.

He knows how hungry they are. The wistful looks they aim at him change suddenly to amusement. Max asks curiously, "What is it? What's wrong?"

"You . . . you put the grain in your pocket, and sand trickled out the hole at the bottom," Onda giggles.

Max peers into the pocket. "There's nothing in there. Are they beach seeds?" He turns to look at the standing crops. The sun is going down, so it is harder to see the mysterious grain. Max lights his lantern jaw. "Why, the cereal is shrinking! They're becoming mini-cereals. It must be an effect of the sunlight."

"In the daytime, they're normal cereals, and at night, they shrink." Wide-eyed, Onda clutches her stomach. "And I was about to eat some of that. Oh, Max, you saved us!"

"It could be," he smiles absently. He is still trying to take a sample of the Daytime Cereals. It won't stay in his pocket, and it falls out between the wicker wands of Onda's basket. "Hmm. I think the only thing it will stay in is the Hope Chest."

"*My* Hope Chest?" Onda asks. "When we're not even sure what it is? You certainly change your mind quickly."

"Well. . . ." Max considers.

*If Max wants to take some Daytime Cereals, and he still has the Two Minute Replay, turn to section 64.*

*If Max wants to take some Daytime Cereals, and the Hope Chest is empty, turn to section 67.*

*If Max doesn't want any Daytime Cereals because he still has the Two Minute Replay, turn to section 72.*

*If he doesn't want any for any reason, turn to section 70.*

## \* **64** \*

"Yes, I do mean your Hope Chest," Max says. "I think that this cereal is more powerful magic than even the Two Minute Replay."

Onda sighs. "I hate to waste it."

"Well, I think this is an important find. We're far more likely to be pursued by something that wants someone to eat, than find ourselves in a situation where two minutes will make that much difference."

"Oh, all right," Onda says reluctantly. She watches as Max lets the shining soap bubble fly out of the box. It pops against a movie trailer, which runs backwards for two minutes, and then switches again to forward, much puzzled.

Carefully, Max shakes the heads of grain into the box. He is amazed by the numbers of kernels that fit now that they have shrunk so in the

darkness. "I think it will make a fine defensive
weapon."

Onda is still not sure, but she returns the Hope
Chest to her basket.

*Turn to section 73.*

## * **65** *

Max's stomach rumbles, and he strips more of
the grain from the stalks. It smells so good, and
he is so hungry! He nibbles a handful of kernels
as Brun and Onda watch anxiously. "That's
funny," he says. "It doesn't taste as good as it
smells."

*Roll 3 D6.*

*If the total is less than or equal to Max's
Constitution, turn to section 63.*

*If greater, turn to section 71.*

# * **66** *

The morning is bright and cheery. Max feels full of energy as he helps Onda gather food from trees they pass as they walk. The whole area is full of busy creatures. Worker bees have a hive under construction, and grasshoppers hop into neat lines along the pathway to fill in broken or bare patches of earth.

Max is lucky enough to find a shirt-tree and replaces his now well-worn rags with a clean, new, cream-colored shirt. A family tree provides him with a coat of arms in warm orange-brown which fits snugly. Onda selects from the shirt-tree a pretty white blouse. To her delight, a dressmaking plant is nearby, and she spends a happy half hour trying on its many blossoms. She ducks behind a small wall-nut tree to put on her choice and emerges in a deep yellow skirt with a brown overskirt and bright red bodice, which look enchanting on her. Max says so and is rewarded with a warm kiss.

The path Onda has located is a broad beaten road through the herbage, which seems to abound thickly here. "I think there's every kind of grass in the world here except Mundane," Onda exclaims, moving her arm to avoid the clutch of a sheaf of crabgrass. The angry little green claws clack in vain, having missed their tender target.

Onda is correct as far as Max can see. The trees are more intermittent, but the luxuriant green ground cover is as thick as fur on a living creature. They examine the earth carefully to make sure they are not walking on a living being's back. Max has read stories about such things, such as sphinxes so large it is a riddle how they ever get enough to eat. The hills and vales of this terrain are easy to traverse, so long as travelers are wary of the vegetation. Witchgrass throws little spells at them that explode in the dirt at their feet. The only awkward moment occurs when one of those spells lands amidst a patch of lemon balm, and the whole side of the road blows up in a loud but sweet-smelling explosion as the balm detonates. Max picks up Onda bodily and flees the scraps of flaming weeds.

They climb a long way on steep grass, which gives them the sensation of ascending a great hill, though the rolling field looks fairly flat and even. With her talent, Onda finds the way out of that particular patch, and they feel themselves descending again.

Clouds begin to build up as they walk down and they're sure it is going to rain very soon. Max looks at the leaden sky and predicts a terrible storm. He runs on ahead of Onda and Brur through the grasslands and finds them a big pillow bush to hide under. He takes Onda's basket and pushes her through a narrow opening into the sheltered interior of the plant. Onda protests the rough handling at first, but discovers she likes her bivouac immensely. With ejaculations of pleasure, Onda crawls around inside the cozy den, plumping up fresh pillows and arranging a neat little nest for them in which they can wait out the storm in comfort.

They are only under cover just in time. Max peers out of the opening to watch the storm rage. The clouds split open with thundering tears, and it begins to hail. At first Max thinks that it is a technicolor hailstorm striking. "Uh oh," he says, watching the pellets strike trees and knock out bits of bark from the trees. The weeping willows sob at such cruel treatment, and a tulip tree purses its mouth wryly. A pair of poet-trees compose modern blank verse to obscure themselves from the storm's view.

"We would have been sorry if there hadn't been shelter close by. We were lucky," Max exclaims. He rubs his pate in sympathy for the trees. The hailstones falling outside his comfortable nest are solid and round, but as soon as any settled to the ground, he can see that they are disk-shaped and shiny orange in color.

"What do you think of that?" Max says, picking up one little disk between his fingers.

"Pennies from heaven." Onda takes it from his hand and turns it over. "Mmm. It smells pretty."

"Sure does. But I thought it would have more than one perfume," Max frowns.

"No, these are one-scent pieces. When it rains tuppennies and sixpennies, then you find ones with more than one scent. Here," Onda hands it back to him with a kiss. "Keep it for good luck." She curls close to Max, and they watch the cloudburst together.

By the time the storm abates, they have had a good rest and are ready to make the final push to the Phantom Ranch.

"We should have a meal while we can," Max insists as they prepare to crawl out of their snug den. "I don't see any pie trees or breadfruit, but right beside this pillow bush is another hot potato plant. We'll get some and have a warm meal before going on. I'm hungry."

"Good idea," Onda agrees, handling her basket with care. "Brun is taking a nap to conserve his strength. Max, I'm worried about him. He is getting very weak."

"I am, too," Max admits, pushing aside the pillows to let Onda out. "Look at this," he says, crawling outside and scooting aside so she can see. "These plants are so close to the pillow bush we didn't really have to leave it."

"That's strange," Onda declares. "Usually pillow bushes don't like to be close to hot plants. Perhaps it isn't hot potatoes. Maybe we'll have to

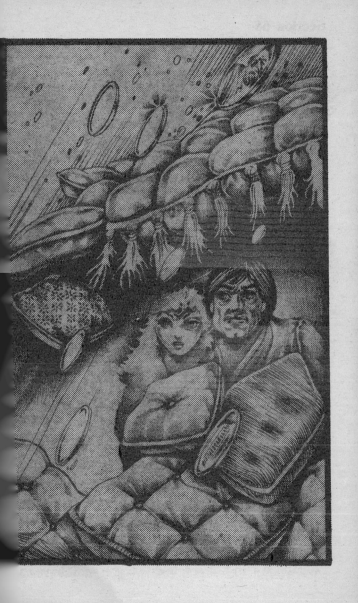

cook these ourselves. But I have no firewater or firewood."

Obediently, Max unearths a tuber or two. They are larger by half than any potatoes he has ever seen, but they aren't hot potatoes. If anything, they feel glassy and cool. Onda takes one and examines it. "The eyes are all turned inward."

"Well, that is strange." Max looks at the other specimen. "Otherwise, they look quite normal."

*If Max decides the potatoes are safe to eat, turn to section 76.*

*If he decides to go on and find other food, turn to section 79.*

## * **67** *

"Yes, well, I do mean your Hope Chest," Max says wistfully. "I think this is powerful and important magic. In the jungles of Xanth, we are likely to be pursued by something that wants to eat us. This fast-growing grain smells so good that any creature would stop to eat it instead."

"Oh, all right," Onda says reluctantly. Unconvinced, she hands him the chest.

Carefully, Max shakes heads of grain into the box. He is amazed by the numbers of kernels that fit now that they have shrunk so in the darkness. "I think it will make a fine defensive weapon."

Onda is still not sure, but she returns the Hope Chest to her basket.

*Turn to section 73.*

*Turn to section 73.*

\* **68** \*

Max's stomach rumbles and pinches like an angry cat-crab, but he turns away from it. "No, better not try any."

"But why not?" Onda asks in exasperation.

"I can't identify it. I've thought and thought, but I can't put a name to this grain. As delicious as it smells, I won't try it."

"Well, what if we eat some, and you take some with you to analyze when you have a chance?" Onda pleads. "I'm so hungry."

"You have to remember how dangerous things in the Xanth jungle can be," Max says apologetically. "It's one of the first things we learned in Centaur School. I've read about so many things that look innocent and are poisonous. Like may-apples and may-not-apples. The former are safe, and the latter are deadly." He throws away the remainder of the cereal and has to jump back when the grains sprout almost instantly at his feet. "Great Xanth!" he exclaims. "What a potential defensive weapon. You can grow grain instantly and distract something that's chasing you with that delicious aroma. Too bad we can't eat them. I'm going to take a sample of it with us. Maybe when we get home Clem Centaur can tell me what it is."

He puts them into his tunic pocket, trying not to be dismayed at the disappointed expressions on Onda's and Brun's faces. The wistful looks they aim at him change suddenly to amusement. Max asks curiously, "What is it? What's wrong?"

"You . . . you put the grain in your pocket, and sand trickled out the hole at the bottom," Onda giggles.

Max peers into the pocket. "There's nothing in there. Are they some kind of beach seeds?" He turns to look at the standing crops. The sun is going down, so it is harder to see the mysterious grain. Max lights his lantern jaw. "Why, the cereal is shrinking! They're becoming mini-cereals. It must be an effect of the sunlight."

"In the daytime, they're normal cereals, and at night, they shrink. Wide-eyed, Onda clutches her stomach. "And I was about to eat some of that. Oh, Max, you saved us!"

Max smiles absently. He is still trying to take a sample of grain. It won't stay in his pocket, and it falls out between the wicker strands of Onda's basket. "Hmm. I think the only thing it will stay in is the Hope Chest."

"*My* Hope Chest?" Onda asks. "When we're not even sure what it is? You certainly changed your mind quickly."

"Well. . . ." Max considers.

*If Max wants to take some Daytime Cereals, and he still has the Two Minute Replay, turn to section 64.*

*If Max wants to take some Daytime Cereals, and the Hope Chest is empty, turn to section 67.*

*If Max doesn't want any Daytime Cereals because he still has the Two Minute Replay, turn to section 72.*

*If he doesn't want any for any reason, turn to section 69.*

* **69** *

"You're right," Max says, apologizing. "I didn't mean to force my idea on you. Besides, why carry the grain with us if we're not positive what it does? It could be very dangerous. Better to leave it alone."

Onda sighs. "Well, I want something I *can* eat. And we ought to start looking for a place to sleep, too."

*Turn to section 73.*

## * **70** *

"I'm sorry," Max said. "Of course it is your Hope Chest. And I'm not really sure I want to carry around something that nearly killed me. Or at least I think that's what would have happened." Max spat to clear the dusty taste out of his mouth.

"Well, I don't want to carry around any grain that I can't eat," Onda pouts. "We really must find food soon."

"Yes. Sometimes I wish I didn't need to eat so much. And we'll want a place to sleep," Max sighs. Not for the first time, he curses the Jack for tricking them. "Let's go."

*Turn to section 73.*

## * **71** *

"How *does* it taste?" Onda asks curiously. "I'm so hungry."

"Well . . . sort of boring," Max admits, looking at the remaining kernels. He makes a sour face. "I'd call it insipid. Don't eat any. I think there's something strange about it, too, something magical."

Max throws down his handful and walks away. Halfway out of the patch, he turns back. "I've made a terrible mistake. I—I need more of that grain," he says desperately. "I have to have more of it."

"What?" Onda demands. "Max, we have to get out of here. The sun is going down, and the bogeys might find us if we don't hurry away."

Max is already picking more of the sweet-smelling cereal and stuffing it into his mouth. "Onda, I have to keep eating this grain. I need it. It's addicted me!" He wrinkles his nose. "It doesn't taste very good, and I don't think there's a whit's worth of nourishment in it, but I can't stop eating it."

"Well, take some with you, and let's get out of here," Onda says, growing frantic. "That colonel didn't like us, and I don't want to see him again. I'm sure he used to be in my nightmares when I was small."

"All right," Max says, pulling grain and filling his pockets with it. The sun is going down quickly now, and they can all see candleberry myrtle and fireweed lighting up in the encampment. At Onda's feet, a line of moonstones springs into incandescence.

"Oh, no, this grain is on their land!" she whispers, as if she fears the bogeys can hear her.

"We'd better get going," Brun says. "The patrol is coming toward us."

"It's all right, Onda," Max assures her, patting

his pockets. "I've got plenty now. We can. . . ."
He looks down. Through holes or tears or
through the weave of the cloth itself, the grains of
the mysterious cereal are sifting out. Max lights
his lantern jaw. "Why, they're shrinking. I'll
never be able to collect enough to feed myself."
Max all but dives at the stalks to collect the
fast-dwindling seeds.

Onda grits her teeth and comes to a decision.
"We'll have to call for help," she decides. "I'm
sorry, Brun, but Max can't go on with the search
if he's sick, and this addiction is a sickness. I only
hope that the healing spring can cure him."

Brun droops sorrowfully, but he concurs. "I'll
just have to go and find Beryl myself. Thank you
for all the help you *have* given me."

Pulling Max down to the ground so they are
hidden from the patrols, Onda releases the snail
with directions for Uncle Buster to find them.
She feels lost and without hope.

*Turn to section 29.*

## * **72** *

"I'm sorry," Max says shamefacedly. "Of course
you are right. I presumed."

"Well, I don't want to throw away the Two
Minute Replay for any silly grain, no matter how

pretty it smells, especially if I can't eat any," Onda pouts.

That brings Max back to reality. "We'd better find food and a place to sleep soon. It is almost dark. I thought I saw some food trees back there, but we don't dare let the bogeys hear us. We'd better move on."

*Turn to section 73.*

## * **73** *

After a long, hungry walk by the light of the waxing moon and Max's chin, the travelers find a grove of wall-nut trees and settle down in the leeward shadow at the corner of two that meet and evidently like one another, for there is no gap between them.

Leaving Brun with Onda, Max hunts up a fruitfly tree. Most of the fruit is asleep for the night and huddle on their stems with their leaves curled. Before they can get away, Max seizes some of the biggest fruitflies, a flying watermelon and a flying canteloupe, and pulls their wings off. He regrets harming living things—it's against his code as a doctor—but Onda and Brun, and not the least, he, have to eat. A few flying plums and cherries are immediately gobbled up to give him the strength to hunt for more food, and Max leaves the tree alone to find something to drink. He can hear the buzzing of the roused fruitflies all the way into the woods.

Much of Xanth is nocturnal and fears bright lights, so Max keeps the intensity of his lantern jaw up to full all the time he is seeking food. He finds a patch of genuine old roats but chose not to take any, nervously remembering the grain in the bogey patch. Instead, he finds a hot potato bush almost by feeling the increased temperature of the ground and pulls up some of the steaming root vegetables. He tosses the potatoes up and down until they are cool enough to carry. He is thinking how good they will taste, especially if he can locate a mature milkweed pod or two and skim the cream off the top.

Just as Max is turning away from the potato bush, something white in the moonlight catches his eye. He swivels back and jumps in fear as a ghost erupts right out of the underbrush, waving its arms in his face.

"Doooon't gooooo!" it shrieks. "Leeeeave the Ghoooost Wriii-ter aloooooone!"

Max gawks at the apparition and swallows hard. Sometimes it is difficult to remember that ghosts are immaterial. This one can't hurt him. Ghosts are only the spirits of beings that die of murder or suicide with their purpose unfulfilled. Max tries to convince himself that it's only a coincidence that it is warning him against the Ghost Writer. How could it know anything about him when its bones must be buried close to the bogey camp? Unless the Ghost Writer is responsible for this ghost's death! Is the mysterious Writer a murderer as well as a kidnapper and a thief?

"Dooooon't goooo!" it groans again and then dissolves into the moonlight. Max is shaken, but he is still resolved to pursue Beryl Bluebird's bird-napper. Jaw set and still gleaming, Max continues to search for food. He rejoins Onda and Brun under the wall-nut. They eat a nervous, lonely meal in the dark grove and go to sleep huddled together. Max does not mention the apparition to the others.

*Turn to section 66.*

## * **74** *

Max's head spins. He didn't realize he was so faint from hunger and his wounds, but it is clear that he is. It seems ironic to him that he should come to the end of his strength surrounded by a field of food, but he doesn't dare eat something he can't identify. In Xanth, that can be fatal. Chokecherries smell delicious, but they choke unsuspecting folk to death when swallowed. And firecrackers catch fire when they're snapped open, even by teeth.

His belly is aching so much, it feels as though it is trying to chew its way out of his body. "Brun,

I'm sorry. Onda, I think you'd better send for help."

Avoiding their sad eyes, Max settles himself down underneath a tree on the outside of the bogeys' barrier, and waits for Onda to release the snail.

*Turn to section 29.*

## * **75** *

With a great effort, Max closes his eyes. His whole body shudders, and his eyelids seem to force themselves open again. Mustering all of his will, Max brings up his empty left hand and covers his eyes. Onda watches with concern. In a moment, his right hand rises as if bearing a great weight and flings the vegetable as far away as it can. Max's body twitches uncontrollably for a few moments, and then he lies still.

"I almost forgot Brun," Max says regretfully. "I almost forgot everything. I would have sat here until I died, letting that silly potato amuse me."

"But what did it do?" Onda wonders, reaching for the other cut half. Max notices it before she can touch it and flings it over the treetops.

"It showed me meaningless entertainment. A magical moving picture with little people falling in and out of love and doing all the things human beings do, only the stories never went anywhere.

I was getting very frustrated, but I couldn't look away! I would have watched it forever. It was almost as powerful as a hypnogourd spell. A cathode-ray tuber! Only I was never swept out of my body. I could hear everything you said, but I didn't care!"

"That's frightening," Onda says, quivering as she realizes that she, too, was almost captured by the potato's spell. "We have to be more careful of strange plants out here in the wilderness."

"Hmm," says Max, picking up the intact potato and tossing it thoughtfully.

"What are you doing?" Onda cries, snatching the vegetable away from him and throwing it away. "You were nearly a zombie, and you're playing with that?"

"I wonder, would these be any good against the Ghost Writer? We will certainly need handier weapons than my tire iron and icicle. He's very powerful and clever, the Jack said." Max speculates. "We'd have to keep it in the Hope Chest, of course, to prevent it from spoiling."

"Or enchanting us," Onda reminds him pointedly.

*If Max wants to take a Couch Potato and leave behind whatever he is carrying in the Hope Chest, turn to section 81.*

*If he chooses not to take along a Couch Potato, turn to section 77.*

## * **76** *

"Perhaps they are cottage potatoes," Max exclaims, handling one interestedly. "One could
use the eyes to see out of instead of windows."
Max draws the icicle and splits the potato in two.
"I've never seen anything like—"

"Like what, Max?" Onda inquires, taking one
half of the vegetable from him. "Max?" He is
staring into the cut side of the half potato with a
blank look on his face. Concerned, she shakes his
arm. "Max!"

"What?" he asks, but his voice is listless and
preoccupied.

"You were just saying you've never seen anything like what?"

"I forget," Max demurs, continuing to gaze at
the potato. Onda, fearing a magical trap like that
of the hypnogourd, puts her hand in front of the
potato. She can see no effect; Max is still cataton-
ic. She tries to snatch away the tuber, but Max's
grip is much stronger than hers. He pushes her
arm away without effort.

"Max, it's enchanted you. Throw it away!"

"I don't want to," Max says, his tone that of a
petulant child. "I like it. It's interesting." As
though it is a puppet, Max's body settles itself
back into a comfortable position against the

pillow bush. His eyes are still staring into the half-potato.

"We have to go," Onda orders. "Brun will die if we don't save Beryl!"

*Roll 3 D6.*

*If the total rolled is less than or equal to Max's value for Intelligence, turn to section 75.*

*If greater, turn to section 80.*

## * **77** *

"True," Max agrees. "Never mind. We'll do our best with what we have."

*Turn to section 82.*

## * **78** *

*Remove one hit point from Max's total for hunger.*

*If his hit points are now reduced to 0, turn to section 74.*

*If he still has hit points left, turn to section 68.*

## * 79 *

At last, Max shakes his head. "I don't want to risk it. We have no idea if they are safe to eat or not." Max knows the journey is telling on both of them, and they need food, but he doesn't want to take a chance on a potential poison. Regretfully, he and Onda set off and look for other things to eat. In verdant Xanth, their next meal should be easy to find.

*Subtract one hit point from Max's total for hunger.*

*If he is reduced to 0 hit points, turn to section 86.*

*If not, turn to section 82.*

## * 80 *

With a great effort, Max attempts to force his eyes shut. His whole body shudders, and his eyelids seem to force themselves open again. Mustering all of his will, Max tries to throw away the potato, but his fingers don't seem to have the power to obey. The vegetable remains tightly clutched in Max's hand. His face contorts mightily and grows red, and cords of sinew stand out on his neck. "It's no use," he says at last, his voice dying away. In a moment, there is a look of peace on his face, and his eyes are as blank as those of the potato.

Onda tries frantically to bring him out of his trance. "Max, Max!" she cries, hoping to get through to his dazzled mind. In time, she has to admit defeat. She reaches into her skirt pocket for the little box containing the fast overland snail and formulates her message for help to Max's father.

*Turn to section 29.*

## * **81** *

"I think we should take one with us," Max says. "Look what a powerful spell it wields. This cathode-ray tuber can capture and enfeeble the mind!"

Onda frowns. "Are you sure it didn't enfeeble yours? It is very dangerous to carry something like that."

"Inside the Hope Chest it won't hurt us." Max fishes out the little box and upends it. He digs up the largest potato he can find and knocks the dirt off of it. It just fits inside the chest, and he locks it in with a firm hand. "There. Now we have a potent weapon."

Onda shakes her head. "I hope you're right."

*Add Couch Potato on the line marked Hope Chest on the character sheet. There can be only one item in the chest at any time.*

*Turn to section 82.*

## \* **82** \*

Onda's map leads them to a stand of trees that she thinks will have wholesome food, and her instinct proves correct. A patch of sugar sand is visible through the ground covering of savory grass in the midst of pie trees and sage-and-onion-brush. Oddly shaped nuts from one tree yield hot and delicious nut meats that taste like the delicacy their shells most resemble. Max cracks the shell of a nut which looks like a fire-chicken and discovers a tender kernel that tastes of chicken. One shaped like a goat-tee, a little beard of moss that will absorb anything, tastes like the best goat. Best of all are the ones shaped like winged buffalo. Buffalo wings are a special delicacy in Max's village. Onda opens one that resembles a bullhorn and is unpleasantly surprised by the noisome nutmeat within. She is happy to exchange it for a fire-chicken.

While they are stuffing themselves with fresh food, Max remembers their almost wedding day and the feast laid out for them then. Onda looked pretty then, but she looks even more beautiful and precious to him now, since she has gone through so much at his side.

"We're almost there," Onda announces indistinctly through a mouthful of peaches-and-cream pie, consulting her map. "Just over the rise is the other clearing. The real Phantom Ranch."

Brun stops pecking at sugar sand and looks up at the humans. He has lost weight since the aborted wedding, and as an animal doctor Max is gravely concerned about the Bluebird's health. Onda had better be right.

When they have eaten and rested, Max leads them up to the crest of the hill. They lie on the ground and survey the valley beyond.

"That's it," Onda whispers. A broad open field, very much like the one in which the Jack had marooned them, lay before them. In the middle of it is a low house with a stable and barn and a large garden. Another small building stands near the garden.

"An aviary," Max exclaims.

Brun wiggles out of Onda's basket and flits joyfully above their heads. "Beryl's in there. I can feel her presence!" For the first time, the

Bluebird's plumage has reached its chromatic zenith. He is the most beautiful blue anyone can imagine. It makes them happy just to look at him, but they can also feel the strength of his magic power. They are overjoyed. "We've got to get down there and let her out!"

"Not so fast," a quavery voice cautions them.

They look around. A tall, thin man with snowy white hair and a pointed salt-and-pepper beard smiles at them, a twinkle in his eye. "Well, my friends, you shouldn't charge in secretly. Why not come in the front door and let me welcome you?"

Onda blushes and titters as he bows over her hand.

"Such a charming and lovely young lady. Please accept these flowers as a tribute from an old man." He proffers a tiny bouquet of white, starlike flowers, shaggy blue blossoms, and larger blooms with big black centers. Onda takes it and breathes in the scent.

"Oh, thank you," she says. "How nice of you. Look, Max! Xanthemums!"

"In token of our everlasting friendship," the old man nods. "Won't you share some of the big flowers with your love there, so he may be part of our happy circle?"

"Of course I will." Onda chooses some of the herbs from her bouquet and hands them to Max.

Max eyes them suspiciously and drops them ostentatiously to the ground. There's something he doesn't like about the old man, who has a seedy and dishonest air about him. "Everlasting friendship and love-will blossoms," he sneers. "Did you think you'd fool us that easily?"

The old man seems undaunted by Max's scorn. "But my dear lad, I have. Look at her. She's my very best friend, aren't you, lovely girl?"

"Yes, yes, I am. I . . . I've never met you before, but I feel that we've always known each other." Onda looks puzzled at what she is saying, but the wrinkles in her brow soon smooth out, and she beams affably at her new friend.

"You see? The forgotten names of herbs and flowers that appear everywhere in Mundania have tremendous power here. A conceit of mine. Another name for love-will is the ghost flower. All of them disguise a mind-bending plant of some power. I am the Ghost Writer, as you must have guessed. You have been looking a long time for me. Come. You must see my garden." He spots Brun suddenly, and his hand goes to the little pouch hanging from his belt. "Oh, how nice, a male Bluebird of Happiness! And such a handsome one. It so happens I have an unattached female who needs a mate. Here, young bird." He holds up another blooming cluster of flowers. "Here's a comfortable clump of bird's-nest to rest on."

"It's an ordinary gold carrot," Max sputters, striking the blossoms and their shining golden root to the ground just before Brun reaches it.

The little bird seems to wake up to the danger and flits quickly out of reach. Max is upset that the kindly old man turns out to be the Ghost Writer in disguise.

"All in the mode of expression," the Writer explains. "It used to be called "bird's-nest." But no matter. If you don't come to me willingly, you will never leave this spot." So saying, he walks away down the hill.

"What a nice man," Onda says, gazing after him, the flowers dangling forgotten from her hand.

"He's crazy," Max corrects her. "We're not going anywhere near him again."

"Oh, Max, why not?"

"Because he's the one who bird-napped Beryl," Max shouts.

"I'm sure he didn't mean to," Onda replies absently, burying her nose in the bouquet.

Max takes the flowers out of her hands and throws them down the slope. Picking up the basket, he grabs Onda by the arm and turns away from the Ranch. "We're leaving. We will come back later when he isn't expecting us, and go straight into the aviary to rescue Beryl." They turn to go down the hill the way they came and discover they are not alone.

Big inverted triangles with mystic notations painted on them block their way. As soon as the travelers face toward them, the fans begin to blow now hot, now cold at them. They flutter in the air without any visible support.

"Stop them," Onda cries, hugging herself for warmth. "I'm freasing!"

"Fantasy fans," Max growls. He draws the icicle. The fans are more of an annoyance than a danger, but they can get in the way, blocking his defense.

"Spec-tackles," Onda gasps, pointing beyond the fans. Those big-shouldered, glassy-eyed monsters surprise their prey by leaping on it and bearing it to the ground. Some of the bamboo blowers were evidently sports fans because they get in Max's way as he attempts to chop at the spec-tackles.

"Take care of Brun," Max shouts as he leaps into the center of the fan group swinging the sickle. If he can take care of these first, he'll be able to fight the spec-tackles more easily. The fans are only made of bamboo, and the sickle should be able to chop them to bits.

His sickle passes right through the fans, which flutter around him, cheekily shooting the breeze through his hair and up his sleeves. "They're not solid," Max exclaims. "They're fan-toms! Mere apparitions."

"So this is what they meant," Brun cries, flying to Onda for shelter. "Mysterious apparitions that haunted her." Onda cuddles the bird to her, backing away from their attackers. The spec-tackles ignore them and move toward Max.

"Look out!" Onda calls. Hearing her voice,

Max glances around and sees the spec-tackles bearing down on him. The fans are flapping back and forth, daunted but not injured by the magic weapon.

"He has enough defenders," Max says grimly, swinging at the spec-tackles. "This Ghost Writer certainly runs an eye-glass operation."

The spec-tackles prove to be spec-tres, Max discovers to his cost as he tries to strike them between their shining lenses. They seem wary of his weapon, but he is not making any perceptible dent in their appearance. He decides that they have been instructed to behave in a certain way; they have no motivation of their own. In fact, he suspects that they are wasting his time for a reason.

"They're not real ghosts," Max pants, after chasing them around the hilltop. "This must be the Ghost Writer's talent: he can generate artificial ghosts. He has to be the source of a ghost I saw two nights ago!"

"What will we do?" Onda wails.

"Nothing. They're not real. They can't hurt you. They're just like any other ghost, but since they never lived, they have no souls. And if they have no souls, they have no magical talents."

"Good," Onda declares, but her voice is trembling. "But what about those?" She extends a fearful hand.

Instantly Max is on guard as he watches the figures approach him. "Wraiths!"

"But wraiths are nocturnal. And these are so tall!"

"Day wraiths are higher than nighttime wraiths," Max explains, then reconsiders as the forms draw closer. "I'm wrong, but it's just as bad. These are zombies."

The skeletal figures dressed in wormy shrouds shuffle up the hill toward Max and Onda. They must be what the apparitions have been waiting for. As the zombies close in, the fan-toms and spec-tres withdraw. In a moment, all that is left of them is the gleam of the glassy eyes of the eye-glass ghosts.

"Leave the girl and the bird alone," Max informs the zombies as they near him. "I'm the only one you need to worry about." He hefts the sickle and hopes they understand him, but zombies' brains are rotten. Only one moves sloppily forward to intercept him. He hopes he can defeat it quickly.

The other zombies stand stupidly by as their chief shambles toward Max. This zombie is less decrepit than his men. He must be more recently dead, Max decides. The others are practically skeletons.

The zombie chief doesn't move too quickly, but he is very good at keeping Max from evading him. For a dead creature, he's quite agile. Max sidesteps, only to have the deteriorating body interpose itself between him and the Phantom Ranch. He tries again, and again the creature cuts off his egress. Against his better nature, for he hates to hurt living or undead things, Max brandishes his sickle and prepares to fight.

**ZOMBIE CHIEF**
*To hit Max: 12   To be hit: 9   Hit Points: 10*

*Max does 1 D6+1 damage with the icicle.*

*The Zombie Chief does 1–3 damage with his club. (Roll 1 D6, divide in half, round up to next largest number.)*

*If Max wins, turn to section 91.*

*If Max loses, turn to section 85.*

*If Max has the Daytime Cereals and wants to use them, turn to section 87.*

*If Max has the Two Minute Replay and wants to use it, turn to section 89.*

\* **83** \*

"Come, come, lad," the Ghost Writer urges him
   "R," Max adds at last.
   "M." The old man has propped his elbows u on the chair arms and is tenting his finger

confidently as if Max has stepped into the trap that has been laid for him.

"A," Max says, but he knows he's lost. Whether the word became 'pharmacy,' or 'pharmacology,' it will end on him. He is a man of honor and accepts that he is beaten. The floating Decimal adjudges accordingly and moves toward Max. He bows his head and fades to intangibility.

"Ah," the Ghost Writer says with satisfaction. "I win. You'll make a lovely addition to my ranch staff, if the spirit moves you. Ha ha ha! Come, I'll show you the rest of my little abode." He walks over to a shelf and takes down a bottle marked 'There Restorer.' He uncorks it and takes a drink. As the liquid runs down his throat, his body resolidifies from his head down to his feet. He is all there once again.

Onda stares with disbelief at what Max has become. The sad figure of her husband glides past her, following the Ghost Writer out of the shadowbox house. The thesaurus winks at her and then goes back to sleep before the glowing firedog.

She runs after them and catches up as the Ghost Writer is giving the silent Max a tour of the garden.

"Maudlin; Sourmint; Rose Madder, both red and blue; constancy dressed all in purple and yellow and white, like your lady love; blue weed and sad sacks; buttercup, which is also called crazy herb; love-lies-bleeding; cuss cuss grass, naughty stuff; happy major; and quaker, poor frightened weed. Not a bad crop. Every emotion known to sentience, and a few of which it is not aware."

*If they have the Two Minute Replay in the Hope Chest, turn to section 92.*

*If they have the Daytime Cereals in the Hope Chest, turn to section 84.*

*If they have the Couch Potato in the Hope Chest, turn to section 94.*

*If they have nothing left in the Hope Chest, turn to section 88.*

* **84** *

"You're a selfish old man," Onda cries fiercely, opening the Hope Chest and flinging the content at his feet. "Take that! You and your spiritou indulgences are finished. That'll fix you," Ond declares, as the Daytime Cereals sprout an grow. "You'll be stuck here. You won't even b able to escape at night because this becomes eve more powerful then. You'll be surrounded fore er by Daytime Cereals, and you won't be able get enough."

The Ghost Writer laughs uproariously, walki

through the spreading patch of grain, arms open wide. "My dear young lady, I have a field twice the size of this house filled with the stuff. These cereals are no good against me. *Most* Daytime Cereals are done by ghost writers. My dear child, we originated the breed. Now, just you amuse yourself for a little while. I have to instruct your disembodied fiancé in his new duties."

Fuming, Onda realizes that her plan has back-fired. She waits until his back is turned, and runs into the house for the bottle of There Restorer. Then she formulates a message to Max's father. It will take time before help arrives, but she needs to be prepared.

*Turn to section 29.*

*Turn to section 29.*

* **85** *

Shedding bits of finger and palm, the zombie matches Max's battle stance, but it waits for him to make the first move. If it fights as slowly as it walks, Max should be able to despatch it in no time.

He swings the icicle in an arc, intending to cut the monster's head from its shoulders. Just before the blade touches its neck, he squeezes his eyes shut, reluctant to watch himself murder another creature. The blade connects with a

*THUNK* instead of a *SWISH*, and Max opens an eyelid to see what happened.

The zombie has its club raised, and Max's sickle is embedded in it. Max curses to himself. He is reluctant to reach forward and free it, since the club is of rotting wormwood, and the worms in it look decrepit enough to be zombies, too. They make him feel sick.

With a strong pull and no evidence of pain in its bony palm, the zombie yanks the sickle blade out and holds it to one side. Max struggles to free his weapon from the zombie's grasp, but it has a deathlike grip. The cold of the sickle doesn't seem to trouble it in the least. While Max is trying to pull his weapon away, the horrible club swings around and clouts him on the back over the kidneys.

"Aagh!" he grunts through clenched teeth. Max staggers back and makes another grab for the sickle, still held blade-first in the zombie chief's fist.

For his troubles, he receives another clout, this time in the ribs. Max blinks, pressing his lips together, trying not to acknowledge the pain, but it is telling on him. He isn't in full health after the last few days' hard journey.

"Max!" Onda screams from behind him. He risks a quick glance to see what is the matter. Several of the zombie guards have her surrounded, and they are forcing her toward the path leading to the Phantom Ranch.

"Stop!" Max shouts. Abandoning the sickle in the zombie's hand, he draws his tire iron and prepares to go to her rescue, but he has forgotten about his own adversary.

The club swings again and clips Max across the back of the head, knocking him unconscious even as he takes the first steps toward Onda.

The girl sees her fiancé fall, and realizes he won't be able to help her. Trying to avoid all contact with her captors, she releases the fast overland snail with a fervent plea for speedy rescue.

*Turn to section 29.*

* **86** *

Max's head spins as he stands up. He didn't realize he was so faint from hunger and the wounds he has suffered, but it is clear that he is. It seems ironic to him that he should come to the end of his strength because of something so silly as a lack of food, but he doesn't dare eat something he can't identify. In Xanth, that can be fatal. Chokecherries smell delicious, but they choke unsuspecting folk to death when swallowed. And firecrackers catch fire when they're snapped open, even by teeth.

His belly is aching so much, it feels as though it

is trying to chew its way out of his body. "Brun, I'm sorry. Onda, I think you'd better send for help."

Avoiding their sad eyes, Max settles himself down and concentrates on ignoring his stomach and waits for Onda to release the snail. For him, the quest is over.

*Turn to section 29.*

* **87** *

Max realizes that this fight could be a long and messy affair. He hasn't time to waste on these decrepit creatures. Brun wants to rescue Bery right away.

He sidesteps the zombie chief. It jumps between him and the pathway to the Ranch, but Max is going the other way.

"Quick, Onda, give me the Hope Chest!"

Puzzled, the girl fumbles in her basket and pops the small box into Max's hands. The zombie chief has almost caught up with him again and Max has little time in which to act, but he is sure the Daytime Cereals will work within the time limit.

Opening the box, he flings its contents away from him. Instantly, the grain begins to sprout out of the ground, maturing and fruiting a heartbeats. Even though Max knows they're dangerous, he is still enticed so much by the scent he has to concentrate to keep from gleaning any for himself to eat.

To look at them, the zombies' sensory organs are long gone, but they seem to be attracted to the aroma as much as he is. Soon, the zombies are all chomping on culled grain and losing teeth, pieces of tongue, and lips all over the place in their eagerness to eat as much of the cereal as they can. Max watches them for a while and is grateful to see that the sight of them completely quells his appetite. One of them bursts his stomach with the bulk of grain and keeps eating happily while his meal falls out of his necrotic alimentary canal. Onda looks quite green, and Brun has his head under his wing.

"Come on," Max tells them. "If that's the best he can throw at us, he's got a lot more to fear from us than we do from him."

*Turn to section 93.*

## * **88** *

Onda stands sadly by. She has no more alternatives, no more weapons she can use to save her fiancé from the Ghost Writer's will. There's nothing left in the Hope Chest, not even hope.

Leaving the Ghost Writer talking to the listless spectre of Max, Onda slips into the house and takes the bottle of There Restorer and hides it in her skirt pocket.

Then she formulates a message to Max's father and releases the snail. It will take time before help arrives, and she needs to be prepared to escape when she can.

*Turn to section 29.*

## * **89** *

Max realizes that this fight could be a long and messy affair. He hasn't time to waste on these decrepit creatures. Brun wants to rescue Ber right away.

He sidesteps the zombie chief. It jumps between him and the pathway to the Ranch, but Max is going the other way.

"Quick, Onda, give me the Hope Chest!"

Puzzled, the girl fumbles in her basket and pops the small box into Max's hands. The zombie chief has almost caught up with him again, and Max has little time in which to act, but he hopes the Two Minute Replay will pull them back far enough in time so they can run down to the Ranch before the zombies appear.

Max opens the box and flings the soap bubble out into the air. It hangs on the breeze for just an iridescent moment, then pops into glittering specks. The sky darkens, and the zombie chief begins to shamble away from him backward. The other zombies hulk backward, too, resuming their stances of two minutes before. Max himself is rushing heels first, restoring the box to Onda's basket, and hastening to stand before the zombie chief at the head of the pass.

The magical effect ends, and Max discovers to his chagrin that he must have spent more than two minutes trying to outmaneuver the zombie chief before he had the bright idea of using the Two Minute Replay. He has wasted it. Now he has no choice but to fight.

**ZOMBIE CHIEF**
*To hit Max: 12   To be hit: 9   Hit Points: 10*

*Max does 1 D6+1 damage with the icicle.*

*The Zombie Chief does 1–3 damage with his club. (Roll 1 D6, divide in half, round up to next largest number.)*

**Section 90**

*If Max wins, turn to section 91.*

*If Max loses, turn to section 85.*

* **90** *

"Come, come, lad," the Ghost Writer urges him.

"N," Max adds at last.

"T, for is this not a phantasy, or a phantasm?"

"O," Max says with deliberate care, for his reality is in the balance. He will not let the old man deliberately mislead him. There is one word which has the right number of letters, and the trap is sprung on the trapper.

"M." The spoken letter has the knell of doom. The Ghost Writer fades into total insubstance like a phantom. His face is black with anger. "This shouldn't happen in real life! Only in fiction! I must rewrite it." He lunges for his type-writer.

All around them, noise, noise which has been absent so long that the racket is painful to the ear, breaks out.

Max hugs Onda, and the two of them run to unlock all the cages of the captive animals and birds. "We can send a message to the Magic-Dust Village so they know where to come and pick up their sad sacks."

Inside the aviary, Brun pecks away furiously at

the wire of a cage containing a single female bluebird. The longer they are close together, the brighter and more colorful their plumage is becoming. Max and Onda burst into the room at last, and the young man unlatches the cage.

"That must be Beryl," Max says, unhooking the other cages and watching his friend and the other bird, now chromatically restored to their glorious azurity, doing a happy aerial dance together.

Beryl lands on Onda and preens coyly. "I thought he'd never come," Beryl warbles. "I was so worried."

"Oh, Max, Onda, how can we ever repay you for reuniting us," Brun says, landing on the young man's shoulder.

"Marry us!" Max exclaims at once, and they all laugh.

There is a loud rumbling underground. "The Ghost Writer's spells are giving way," Onda exclaims. Outside the aviary, the ghosts and zombies and other creatures are wandering around aimlessly, and the disembodied spectre of the Ghost Writer is running from one to another of them and screaming orders, all of which are being ignored in the confusion. The humans and the birds dash out of the clearing and to safety, where Onda releases the snail with a triumphant message for Max's father.

Brun and his lady bird spend a happy afternoon until Uncle Buster's balloon comes into view. The travelers climb into it and greet their rescuer with joy.

Uncle Buster looks into their ecstatic faces and chuckles. "Shall I finish the wedding ceremony right here? You'll be the only couple in Xanth joined by two Bluebirds of Happiness."

"They deserve it," says Brun, fluttering up to perch on Max and Onda's joined hands. "If it hadn't been for them, I would no longer be a blue bird. Or a happy one," he adds, as Beryl lands next to him.

"Well, then, I'll continue where we left off," Buster declares. "By the power vested in me by the King and Kingdom of Xanth, I proclaim this man and this woman to be husband and wife."

"And may they enjoy eternal happiness with one another," Brun says, suffusing everyone present with joy.

"And that goes double for me," Beryl adds, making them twice as happy. "Whew! That felt good. I haven't been able to use my magic in so long! Say, we'd better get to the Magic-Dust Village right away. I have a dozen weddings to perform. Those couples will have been waiting for weeks!" She and Brun nestle together on the rim of the eggshell, each Bluebird now more blue than the other from pure joy. "And then we have a blue moon to make up for." She looks shyly at her mate.

Brun glows at her. "Yes, we have."

"Whatever you say, lady bird," Buster says

agreeably, turning the balloon for the north. "There'll also be a wedding feast you're invited to attend up at the South Village, if you desire. How about it, Max, Onda? Any objections to a diversion?"

There is no answer. Max and Onda are locked in each other's arms, kissing passionately.

"I suppose not," Buster grins. "Married at last! An unconscionable delay, I must say. Glad to have you back in the world again, Beryl. Well, then, the Magic-Dust Village it is. Did I ever tell you young birds about the time my wife and I flew up to Castle Roogna? No? Well, then, it was on a fine summer's day like this one. . . ."

The balloon gathers more hot air and sails gaily up into the sky.

The End

* **91** *

Shedding bits of finger and palm, the zombie matches Max's battle stance, but it waits for him to make the first move. If it fights as slowly as it walks, Max should be able to despatch it in no time.

He swings the icicle in an arc, intending to cut the monster's head from its shoulders. Just before the blade touches its neck, Max squeezes his eyes shut, reluctant to watch himself murder another creature. The blade connects with a *THUNK* instead of a *SWISH*, and Max opens an eyelid to see what happened.

The zombie has its club raised, and Max's sickle is embedded in it. Max curses to himself. He is reluctant to reach forward and free it, since the club is of rotting wormwood, and the worms in it look decrepit enough to be zombies, too. The sight makes him feel sick.

With a strong pull, Max hauls on the sickle's handle and wrenches it free of the club's mouldy surface. Several worms come flying out, and part of the zombie's arm and one of its kneecaps fall to the ground. Max isn't worried. A zombie's magic is that it can go on dropping parts forever; the pieces regenerate, though in a more decrepit condition than before.

That fact is also to his disadvantage. He will have to chop the zombie nearly to bits to defeat it. With no taste for his task, he starts by slashing through the rest of the arm holding the wormwood club.

The zombie doesn't appear to suffer any pain from the amputation. It merely picks up the club with its other hand and counters Max when he goes to run around it. Frustrated, Max chops away at its head and neck. Pieces daubed with horrible goo fly off in every direction, but the creature keeps up with Max.

Finally, Max gets an inspiration. He leads with

a blow at the nearly headless monster's shoulders, and instead, sweeps it underneath at its decaying lower limbs. He manages to slice deeply into its thigh and through a bone before the club moves in to intercept. He repeats the ruse on the other side, and deprived of adequate support for its tattered body, the zombie collapses to the ground.

That isn't the end of it, though. It pounds the ground determinedly, attempting to strike at Max, but he moves easily out of range. It crawls forward, shedding gobbets of flesh, using the stumps of its severed arm and legs.

"Come on, Onda." Max takes the girl's hand and leads her away from the grisly remains of the zombie, which is still trying to stop him. Nauseated, Max escorts Onda down the hill.

*Turn to section 93.*

* **92** *

The time is running out, but Onda is sure that she can reverse the outcome of the game if she is quick. Opening the Hope Chest, she flings the bubble in the direction of the Ghost Writer and Max. The sky darkens.

The three of them move backward, duplicating precisely the actions they have just played through. Onda pays close attention as the last round of the Ghost game is replayed, and bites her lip as she concentrates on a strategy she has in mind. If only Max remembers the right spellings!

"A." Max unbows his head and inhales the letter. The infinite Decimal hangs quivering in the air.

"M." The letter sounds odd, said backward.

"R," Max says, and a long time passes before the Ghost Writer speaks.

"Dal, emoc, emoc." The sky outside lightens again, and the Ghost Writer reverses the phrase. "Come, come, lad," he says for the second time. Onda is jubilant. The man has no idea that anything strange has happened.

"R," Max says, after a long pause.

"Hurry up," Onda blurts out to the Ghost Writer.

The man looks surprised that she is speaking to him. "Why?" he asks.

"Y?" Max inquires, concentrating. "Is that your letter?"

The Writer is still gazing at Onda, head cocked to one side. "Yes, yes, certainly."

Max sticks his tongue out of the side of his mouth, and Onda knows he is counting. "N," he decides.

The Ghost Writer opens and closes his mouth. It is clear he is counting, too. He doesn't know how she did it, but he is positive Onda knew what he was going to say, and tricked him into saying another letter. "X," he says, his face black with wrath. "This only happens in real life! Not in fiction. I must rewrite it." He lunges for his type-writer, but he is just a moment too late.

The Decimal zips over to him, and he fades out of substance entirely.

All around them, noise, noise which has been absent so long that the racket is painful to the ear, breaks out.

"I hear Beryl's voice," Brun warbles and flies out the door. Max follows right behind him. Onda comes out a moment afterward.

"What did you do?" Max whispers as they rush out of the house.

Onda shows him the empty Hope Chest and the There Restorer. "I had a little spare time," she smiles impishly. "He'll be busy for a while wondering where this bottle is. All sorts of things are breaking loose in there. We'd better hurry."

Max hugs her, and the two of them run to unlock all the cages of the captive animals and birds. "We can send a message to the Magic-Dust Village so they know where to come and pick up their sad sacks."

Inside the aviary, Brun pecks away furiously at the wire of a cage containing a single female bluebird. The longer they are close together, the brighter and more colorful their plumage is becoming. Max and Onda burst into the room at last, and the young man unlatches the cage.

"That must be Beryl," Max says, unhooking the other cages and watching his friend and the other bird now brilliantly colored, doing a happy aerial dance together.

Beryl lands on Onda and preens coyly. "I thought he'd never come," Beryl warbles. "I was so worried."

"Oh, Max, Onda, how can we ever repay you for reuniting us," Brun says, landing on the young man's shoulder.

"Marry us!" Max exclaims at once, and they all laugh.

There is a loud rumbling underground. "His spells are giving way," Onda exclaims. Outside the aviary, the ghosts and zombies and other creatures are wandering around aimlessly, and the disembodied spectre of the Ghost Writer is running from one to another of them and screaming orders, all of which are being ignored in the confusion. The humans and the birds dash out of the clearing and to safety, where Onda releases the snail with a triumphant message for Max's father.

Brun and his lady bird spend a happy afternoon until Uncle Buster's balloon comes into view. The travelers climb into it and greet their rescuer with joy.

Uncle Buster looks into their ecstatic faces and

chuckles. "Shall I finish the wedding ceremony right here? You'll be the only couple in Xanth joined by two Bluebirds of Happiness."

"They deserve it," says Brun, fluttering up to perch on Max and Onda's joined hands. "If it hadn't been for them, I would no longer be a blue bird. Or a happy one," he adds, as Beryl lands next to him.

"Well, then, I'll continue where we left off," Buster declares. "By the power vested in me by the King and Kingdom of Xanth, I proclaim this man and this woman to be husband and wife."

"And may they enjoy eternal happiness with one another," Brun says, suffusing everyone present with joy.

"And that goes double for me," Beryl adds, making them twice as happy. "Whew! That felt good. I haven't been able to use my magic in so long! Say, we'd better get to the Magic-Dust Village right away. I have a dozen weddings to perform. Those couples will have been waiting for weeks!" She and Brun nestle together on the rim of the eggshell, each Bluebird now more blue than the other out of pure joy. "And then we have a blue moon to make up for." She looks shyly at her mate.

Brun glows at her. "Yes, we have."

"Whatever you say, lady bird," Buster says agreeably, turning the balloon for the north. "There'll also be a wedding feast you're invited to attend up at the South Village, if you desire. How about it, Max, Onda? Any objections to a diversion?"

There is no answer. Max and Onda are locked in each other's arms, kissing passionately.

"I suppose not," Buster grins. "Married at last! An unconscionable delay, I must say. Glad to have you back in the world again, Beryl. Well, then, the Magic-Dust Village it is. Did I ever tell you young birds about the time my wife and I flew up to Castle Roogna? No? Well, then, it was on a fine summer's day like this one. . . ."

The balloon gathers more hot air, and sails gaily up into the sky.

### The End

### * **93** *

The Phantom Ranch looks homey after all the rustic and wild places Max and Onda have visited over the last few days. Max has to rein himself back to keep from relaxing. This is the citadel of the enemy they have come here to stop. But it is a nice place. The huge gardens are attractively kept, and white-sheeted ghosts float gently through the paths of a herb maze.

The door to the house stands open, and Max stands to one side and listens. There is a mysteri

ous clacking noise and the sound of water bubbling.

"Come in, come in," the cheery voice of the
Ghost Writer invites them.

Max is unpleasantly surprised to realize he has
known all the time that they are there. Warily, he
leads Onda inside.

"Welcome, welcome at last. You are my ghests
and I am your g-host!" The Ghost Writer chortles.

"Ghastly," gulps Max, keeping his courage up
for Onda's sake.

"Exactly," smiles the Ghost Writer, folding his
long hands over the beginnings of a pot belly.
"Please, make yourselves at home. Since you're
not leaving, this *is* your home. Your new home. I
hope you like it. In my youth, people always said
I was 'bound for the warm place,' and indeed I
keep it as warm as I can."

In a cozy room which they would have found
most comfortable under any other circumstances, the Ghost Writer sits at a table poking
with the fingers of both hands at a Mundane
philosophical device Max recognizes as a type-
writer. Behind him is a large stove with a con-
tented firedog curled in the open belly generating
heat. On top of the stove, a large cauldron
bubbles furiously.

"Yes, I'm glad to meet a man of knowledge,"
the Writer admits pleasantly. "I decide what *type*
of ghost I want, and then I *write* it. It's how I

manifest my talent. You saw some of my handiwork a few nights ago and again just at the top of the hill. Good, aren't they?" He notices their gaze move to the cauldron. "Oh, yes, and that's where I create my potboilers. Very popular among those who want a good scare, but nothing serious. Sometimes steamy, but a lot of hot air," the Ghost Writer sketches a loop with his long fingers, "though it can give some ladies the vapors. You should try one. You might like it. Allow me to choose one for you."

"You make ghosts to order?" Onda asks, astonished.

"Oh, yes. Ever since I discovered my talent. I supply seances, campfire ghost storytellers, mothers who want their children to behave—oh, all sorts of people. There used to be a great deal of demand for my work from Mundania, but that's fallen off. They have enough horror of their own. Mine is but small doings compared with what they see every day."

"That doesn't explain why you're birdnapping, and stealing crops and all the other things we've heard about you," Onda points out.

The Writer smiles fondly at her. "It has everything to do with it. I crave an audience for my talents. But to induce craving, I need to be able to compel emotion. And to do that, I've been gathering all the magic of Xanth that has to do with emotions. Plants, animals, spirits, and minerals. Human beings are ruled by their emotions, and fairly soon, I shall rule all emotions, so I shall rule all humans and part-humans in Xanth through them. They shall not be able to feel cheer or sadness, unless I will it. Nor hate, nor love, nor guilt, nor hope, nor despair . . . no, I take that back. They should be feeling their own despair."

"That's horrible!"

"Thank you, my dear," the Ghost Writer says, bowing to her from his chair. "Now, if you'll excuse me, I have a lot of work to do." He looks at the sheet of parchment rolled into the top of the type-writer, and bends down to consult a small dinosaur curled up at his feet.

"Theo, I need a better word than 'conquer.' "

"Horse chestnut," the little creature yawns.

"Wrong spelling, thesaurus. Conquer, not conker."

"Conquer," the beast repeats. "Defeat, sub-due, usurp."

"Good. That's just what I shall do to Xanth." The old man cackles and goes back to his work.

"He's ignoring us," Max says in disbelief.

"Obviously he doesn't think that we're any kind of a threat," Onda opines.

Max hefts his tire iron. "I'll show him we're a threat. We've got to save Beryl and get out of here to warn everyone what the Ghost Writer is up to!"

"How do you think you're going to do that?" Onda asks, worried. "This place is well pro-tected."

"He's not." Max tosses the iron and catches it and walks over to the engrossed Writer. "Excuse me. I can't let you take over Xanth. We like it the way it is. I challenge you to a duel."

"Sorry, laddie. I was changing a character. What can I do for you?"

"I challenge you to a duel," Max repeats stoutly.

"A duel? My dear young man, do you imagine that I'd let a frail old codger like myself suffer a physical beating at the hands of a young and strapping ogre like yourself? I certainly won't let you near me with weapons."

Max's feelings are hurt. He knows he is much handsomer than an ogre. He is reluctant to strike the man with the tire iron, and his opponent knows it and is somehow controlling his feelings. "Well," Max reasons, struggling to contain his ire, "I must defeat you. And I can't think of any other way."

"Wrong. You seem to be rather precise with words. Yours was the challenge, so mine is the choice of weapons. Words. Not your magical steel," the Writer says distastefully. "Yes, words it will be. That way we'll both be armed adequately."

Max narrows an eye suspiciously at him but puts the iron back in the sheath. "How can I trust you?"

"Me? Don't trust me. I've had a lifetime to bend words to my bidding." The old man chortles, and opens a box. Out of it, he draws a infinitesimal black dot. "This is the Infinite Decimal. My choice of weapons is the game of Ghost. You and I will spell out words at one another. Say I start with G, you respond H, I counter with O, you say S, and I must finish with T. That would make me G, or one-fifth of a Ghost.

"Naturally, the object is not to finish words, but to make your opponent do it. The Decimal is precise and completely impersonal. It will adjudge our contest and remove the appropriate fraction of your reality. The one who becomes five-fifths of a Ghost is the loser. If you win, I will let the lady bird go, and all my present collection of herbs and animals, and begin again to mold my conquest of Xanth. At my age, the chances of completing it again are slim. That's what you wish, isn't it? But if I win, you will serve me here as one of my ghosts, and your Bluebird will join all of mine in captivity. Is it worth the risk?"

Max thinks for a moment. He is a good speller, almost the best student Clem Centaur had ever had. On the other hand, the Ghost Writer won't have suggested the game if he wasn't sure of winning. Max probably doesn't have the ghost of a chance of winning. "Very well," he declares. "I accept your terms."

"Very well," the old man echoes, "let the duel begin. You may go first," the Ghost Writer says graciously.

"G," Max states.

"O," adds the Ghost Writer, almost offhand.

Good, thinks Max. He's going to spell 'goblin' or 'gobble.' Either way it'll land on him, and that will be his first part of a Ghost. "B."

Suddenly, Max feels himself sink partway into the floor. The Ghost Writer peers at him merrily. "Perhaps you had better sit in one of my chairs. They're ghostproof. If you're not used to being insubstantial, I recommend it highly."

Max had lost the first round, but how? "Gob isn't a real word. It's slang for 'mouth.'"

"I'm afraid even the thesaurus will disagree with you, Max," the Writer said, petting the ugly little dinosaur. "Tell him, Theo."

"Gob. Accumulation, amount, ball, bite, lump, mouth, piece, sailor." The lizard creature spouts out his definitions and curls up again at his master's feet.

Max nods reluctant acceptance. "All right. I won't be that careless again." He makes his way to the indicated chair and sinks into it, but only as far as he would if he had been entirely substantial. It is comfortable, but Max doesn't want to relax. He is gambling with the life of his wife and friends.

"W," the Writer says, starting the next round.

"R," returns Max.

"A."

Max thinks hard. He had almost said, "P," or "I," for wrap or wraith, but realizes that the Decimal would decide against him once more if he did either. "T," he says firmly.

## Section 93

"Well done, young challenger. I have no choice but H." Chuckling, the old man becomes slightly transparent. "Now we're both one-fifth of a Ghost."

"B," says Max, concentrating.

"L."

"E." Max tries to look confident, intending to psych out the Writer.

His opponent only smiles. "N."

"C." He almost said, "D." This answer flung the challenge back at the enemy.

"H." The Ghost Writer whitens and becomes more transparent, and Max can see the chairback through the old man's body.

The duel goes on until Max and the Ghost Writer are nearly invisible. Max is finding it hard to keep up. His skill at spelling begins to falter as his solidity slips away. They have reached the deciding round, and Max is holding on to reality with all his might.

"P," says his opponent.

"H," Max returns, after thinking deeply.

"A."

*Roll 3 D6.*

*If the total is greater than Max's value for Intelligence, turn to section 83.*

*If less than or equal to his Intelligence, go to section 90.*

# * 94 *

"It'll never work," Onda taunts him.

"Certainly it will. I've worked for years to bring my plan to fruition."

"Just words," Onda sneers.

"Of course," the Ghost Writer says airily. "I intend to control all emotions in Xanth, by moving them with my words."

"I'll buy them from you," she offers.

"What have you got that I could possibly want?"

"One picture is worth a thousand words," Onda says, producing the Couch Potato. She cuts it open with Max's pocket knife, careful not to look into it herself, though if it failed to stop the Ghost Writer, she didn't care what happened to her.

"Isn't this interesting?" the Writer murmurs, turning it over and examining it. "How is this worth all of my words—?" Then his eyes are drawn by the cut side. From where Onda stands, she can't see whatever it is he is looking at, but his mind is now in thrall. "But wait," the Writer cries, attempting unsuccessfully to throw the potato away. "You can't leave me here with this meaningless nonsense. I can't break free!"

"I can and I will," Onda tosses her head. "You were going to keep my husband as a disembodied entity here to mind your garden. I want him with me!"

"You shall have him! Free me!"

"No way. Your spiritous indulgences are at an end." Onda ignores his pleas and runs into the house. From the shelf, she retrieves the bottle of There Restorer, and brings it to Max.

His hands slip right through the bottle, so she has to hold it steady for him. But it takes only a sip, and Max is himself again.

Max hugs her tight, rejoicing in physical being once more, and the two of them run to unlock all the cages of the captive animals and birds. "We can send a message to the Magic-Dust Village so they know where to come and pick up their sad sacks."

Inside the aviary, Brun pecks away furiously at the wire of a cage containing a single female bluebird. The longer they are close together, the brighter and more colorful their plumage is becoming. Max and Onda burst into the room at last, and the young man unlatches the cage.

"That must be Beryl," Max says, unhooking the other cages and watching his friend and the other bird doing a happy aerial dance together.

Beryl lands on Onda and preens coyly. "I thought he'd never come," Beryl warbles. "I was so worried."

"Oh, Max, Onda, how can we ever repay you for reuniting us," Brun says, landing on the young man's shoulder.

"Marry us!" Max exclaims at once, and they all laugh.

There is a loud rumbling underground. "His spells are giving way," Onda exclaims. Outside the aviary, the ghosts and zombies and other creatures are wandering around aimlessly. The humans and the birds dash out of the clearing and to safety, where Onda releases the snail with a triumphant message for Max's father.

Brun and his lady bird spend a happy afternoon until Uncle Buster's balloon comes into view. The travelers climb into it and greet their rescuer with joy.

Uncle Buster looks into their ecstatic faces and chuckles. "Shall I finish the wedding ceremony right here? You'll be the only couple in Xanth joined by two Bluebirds of Happiness."

"They deserve it," says Brun, fluttering up to perch on Max and Onda's joined hands. "If it hadn't been for them, I would no longer be a blue bird. Or a happy one," he adds, as Beryl lands next to him.

"Well, then, I'll continue where we left off," Buster declares. "By the power vested in me by the King and Kingdom of Xanth, I proclaim this man and this woman to be husband and wife."

"And may they enjoy eternal happiness with one another," Brun says, suffusing everyone present with joy.

"And that goes double for me," Beryl adds, making them twice as happy. "Whew! That felt good. I haven't been able to use my magic in so long! Say, we'd better get to the Magic-Dust Village right away. I have a dozen weddings to perform. Those couples will have been waiting for weeks!" She and Brun nestle together on the rim of the eggshell, each Bluebird now more blue than the other out of pure joy. "And then we have a blue moon to make up for." She looks shyly at her mate.

Brun glows at her. "Yes, we have."

"Whatever you say, lady bird," Buster says agreeably, turning the balloon for the north. "There'll also be a wedding feast you're invited to attend up at the South Village, if you desire. How about it, Max, Onda? Any objections to a diversion?"

There is no answer. Max and Onda are locked in each other's arms, kissing passionately.

"I suppose not," Buster grins. "Married at last! An unconscionable delay, I must say. We expected them to be well off on their wedding trip by now. Glad to have you back in the world again, Beryl. Well, then, the Magic-Dust Village it is. Did I ever tell you young birds about the time my wife and I flew up to Castle Roogna? No? Well, then, it was on a fine summer's day like this one. . . ."

The balloon gathers more hot air, and sails gaily up into the sky.

**The End**